Science — Staged Assessment
Year 10

This book is for anyone doing OCR GCSE Science — Staged Assessment.

We've stuck in loads of questions on
all the _really important stuff_ that
could turn up in your Exam.

Then we had a real good stab at trying
to make it a bit funny — so you'll _actually use it_.
Simple as that.

CGP are just the best

The central aim of Coordination Group Publications is to produce
top quality books that are carefully written, immaculately
presented and marvellously funny — whilst always making sure they
exactly cover the specification for each subject.

And then we supply them to as many people as we possibly can,
as _cheaply_ as we possibly can.

Buy our books — they're ace

Contents
Year 10 Workbook

Contents
Year 10 Workbook

Contributors:

Matthew Ball

Chris Bates MMath (Hons) GIMA

Charley Darbishire BA (Hons)

Gemma Hallam MA Hons. (Cantab)

Simon Little BA (Hons)

Toby Langley BSc (Hons)

Tim Major BSc (Hons)

Tessa Moulton BSc (Hons)

Pratheeban Nambyiah BA (Hons)

Alison Palin

Andy Park BSc (Hons)

Sam Patterson

Philip Robson

Julie Schofield

Claire Thompson BSc

Suzanne Worthington BSc (Hons)

Based on original questions by:

Jane Cartwright

Chris Christofi

Bill Doling

Alex Kizildas

Nigel Saunders

Published by Coordination Group Publications Ltd

ISBN   1 84146 959 9

Groovy Website: www.cgpbooks.co.uk

Printed by Elanders Hindson, Newcastle upon Tyne.

Clipart sources: CorelDRAW and VECTOR.

Proofreading by:

David Worthington BSc (Hons) PhD MCB FRCPath CChem FRSC

Eileen Worthington BSc (Hons) PGCE

Cells

Q1   Answer this question about **human cells**.

a)   Match the following descriptions to the correct parts of the cell.

   1)   Cytoplasm   **i)**   Controls the passage of substances in and out of the cell.
   2)   Nucleus   **ii)**   Place where most chemical reactions take place.
   3)   Cell membrane   **iii)** Place where the genetic information is stored.

b)   Label the different parts on the diagram of a human cell:

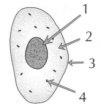

Q2   There is one white cell to every 600 red cells in the blood. That's still quite a lot! White blood cells are involved in protecting the body against infection.

   How are white blood cells adapted to engulf microbes?

Q3   The diagram on the right is of a leaf cell.

   Copy and label the diagram using these words:
   cell membrane; cell wall; chloroplast; cytoplasm; nucleus; sap vacuole

Q4   These are two **single-celled** organisms that swim in water.

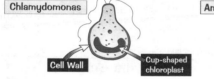

a)   Which one is more like a **plant cell**?
b)   Give **two** reasons **why**.
c)   Give three components that both plant and animals cells have.

Q5   **Red blood cells** are **biconcave** in shape — they curve inward on both sides. They are also unusual because they have **no nucleus**. Oxygen **diffuses** across the membranes of red blood cells, which then carry the oxygen to different parts of the body. These cells travel down capillaries which are only slightly wider than the cells.

   Give one possible reason for:
   i) the **shape** of the cell.
   ii) the **lack** of a nucleus.

Q6   Complete the **blanks** using the words below (words may be used more than once).

| cell membrane | palisade | | top | cell wall |
| chloroplasts | cytoplasm | sap | nucleus | vacuole |

   Virtually all plant and animal cells have a _____, cytoplasm and a _____.
   Plant cells are strengthened by a cellulose_____. They also have a large, permanent
   _____ which contains _____. This is a liquid that contains stored
   substances and water. The water provides support for the cell. Chemical processes take
   place in the _____. The _____ carries genetic information.
   It contains chromosomes which carry genes — the genes control characteristics. Plants
   make their food by photosynthesis. The _____ cells contain many _____ and
   are positioned towards the _____ of the leaf to maximise light absorption.

The Digestive System

We all need food — but do you know what happens to it once you've got it into your body?

Q1   One of the purposes of the **digestive system** is to break down food.

Where is food first broken down? **Describe** this process.

Q2   The diagrams below show the major parts of the digestive system.

D shows the mouth, salivary glands and the oesophagus.
Identify the other labelled parts, and write down their **letter** and **name**.

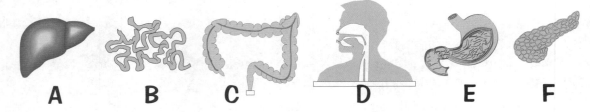

A　　**B**　　**C**　　**D**　　**E**　　**F**

Q3   These are the parts of the digestive system that food actually goes through.

a)   Draw arrows to match each part to its correct function:

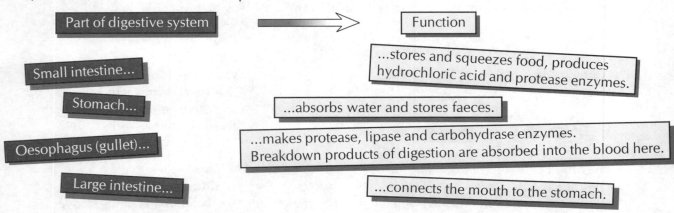

Part of digestive system　　→　　Function

Small intestine...

Stomach...

Oesophagus (gullet)...

Large intestine...

...stores and squeezes food, produces hydrochloric acid and protease enzymes.

...absorbs water and stores faeces.

...makes protease, lipase and carbohydrase enzymes.
Breakdown products of digestion are absorbed into the blood here.

...connects the mouth to the stomach.

b)   **Write down** the parts of the digestive system with their function **in the order** they would work to digest some food.

c)   **Where** do digested food molecules go to after leaving the intestines?

Q4   Look at the diagram below. It shows a bolus of food moving through the inside of the oesophagus.

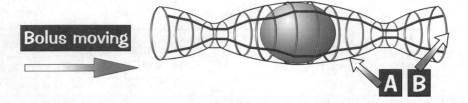

Bolus moving

A B

a)   The labels A and B point to two types of **muscle**. Name A and B.

b)   What is the name given to the muscular process that forces food through the digestive system?

The Digestive System

More on the digestive system I'm afraid — and no pictures either...

Q5 What is an **enzyme**?

Q6 What is **chemical digestion**? What are **digestive** enzymes?

Q7 When starch, proteins and fats enter the body they are **converted** to glucose, amino acids, fatty acids and glycerol. Explain why this is necessary.

Q8 **Gastric juice** is added to food when it reaches the stomach. This juice contains an acid.

  a) Name the acid secreted by the stomach.
  b) Give two reasons why the stomach secretes this acid.
  c) Estimate the pH of the stomach contents, and give a reason for your answer.

Q9 It is **difficult** for lipase to digest fat. Enzymes work in solution, but fat does not dissolve in water. If fat can be broken up into smaller droplets, lipase can digest the fat more effectively.

  a) **Bile** emulsifies fat. What does **emulsify** mean?
  b) What happens to the surface area of fat when it is **emulsified**?
  c) Explain why bile allows lipase to **digest** fats more effectively.

Q10 As well as emulsifying fats, **bile** also speeds up digestion in another way.

  a) Acid is added to food in the stomach. What effect does bile have on this?
  b) Explain how this increases the rate of digestion.

Q11 Enzyme activity is affected by many different factors.

  a) How does temperature affect enzyme activity?
    Draw a graph of enzyme activity against temperature and label the optimum point (see below).
  b) Draw a graph of enzyme activity against pH.
  c) What can happen to enzyme activity at high temperature (and extremes of pH)?
    Label 45°C on your first graph and explain why this is a significant temperature.

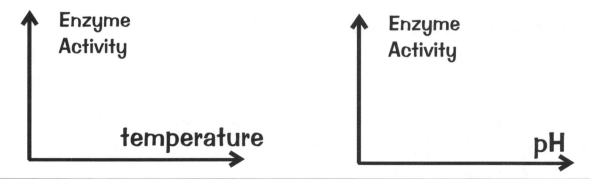

Starch, proteins, fats — so much to digest...

There's a lot to remember on these pages, including some <u>strange long names</u>. But <u>don't</u> be tempted to cut corners, because you really need to know all this stuff. Go through it all bit by bit — you need to be able to remember <u>all</u> the details about digestion. Knowing about enzymes is important too.

The Digestive System

This is the final page on digestion — just grin and swallow it...

Q12 Match each nutrient to its correct form when digested:

Starch is digested to form...

...smaller molecules called fatty acids and glycerol.

Protein is digested to form...

...smaller molecules called sugars.

Fat is digested to form...

...smaller molecules called amino acids.

Q13 The diagram to the right shows the organs used in digestion.

Copy the diagram. Use words from the following list to label it. The bile duct has already been done for you.

> gall bladder   stomach
> small intestine   pancreas

Label the stomach, small intestine and pancreas with the enzyme(s) that they produce from the list below.

> Carbohydrase (amylase)
> protease (pepsin)   lipase

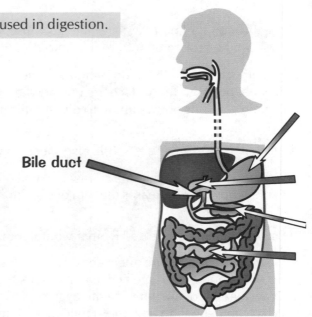

Bile duct

Q14 The products of digestion are absorbed into the bloodstream.

a) In **which part** of the digestive system does this happen?

b) The various digestive juices add greatly to the volume of water taken in by eating and drinking. **Where** in the digestive system is **excess water** absorbed?

c) What do you think will happen if **too much** water is absorbed?

d) What about if **too little** water is absorbed?

Don't just sit there — get off your pancreas and learn it...

The final few details on digestion are pretty simple to learn — start by <u>learning</u> what the different nutrients are broken down into, and then the diagram above. Once you can answer all of these questions easily <u>from memory</u>, just learn the final section. Easy marks to be picked up here.

Lungs and Breathing

Breathing — vital work, just like these questions. So make sure you can do both.

Q1   **Copy and complete** the passage below about the **breathing system**.
Choose the correct word from each highlighted pair.

> The breathing system takes **air** / **oxygen** into and out of the body.
> This allows **carbon dioxide** / **oxygen** to pass from the air into the bloodstream,
> and **carbon dioxide** / **oxygen** to pass out of the bloodstream into the air.

Q2   The diagram to the right represents the **thorax**.

a)   Which **organ** would normally be found in the space at **X**?

b)   **Match** up the letters **A — G** with the correct labels given below:

- alveoli
- bronchiole
- bronchus
- diaphragm
- lung
- rib
- trachea

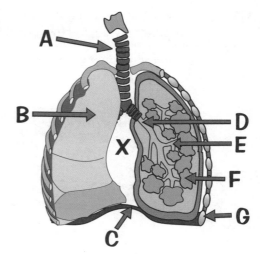

Q3   Here's a question on the **structure** of the lungs:

a)   What feature of the thorax **protects** the lungs from external damage?

b)   What feature of the thorax separates the **lungs** from the **abdomen** (lower part of the body)?

c)   How do the bronchi and bronchioles stay open when their internal pressure falls?

Q4   You breathe in through your nose or your mouth.
Air passes through parts of your breathing system to the **alveoli**.

Put these parts of the breathing system in the **correct order**:

bronchioles   trachea   bronchi   alveoli

Q5   Answer these questions about **air passages**:

a)   Give **another name** for the trachea.

b)   The trachea splits into smaller passages called **bronchi** (one on its own is called a **bronchus**).
How many bronchi are there in each lung?

c)   What is a **bronchiole**?

d)   What is an **alveolus**?

Lungs and Breathing

Don't say I never give you any practical experiments to do — try this one: breathe in, breathe out...

Q6 We each have over 300 million **alveoli** in the lungs. This ensures that enough oxygen diffuses into our bloodstream and that the waste carbon dioxide is removed .

Explain how the **structure** of the alveoli allows this gas exchange between air and blood to happen quickly.

Q7 Look at the sentences below. They are all to do with movements of the thorax and diaphragm when we **breathe in**, but to make things tricky they've been muddled up.

Write the sentences in the correct order.

This pulls the ribcage upwards.

The intercostal and diaphragm muscles contract.

Atmospheric air enters the lungs.

These two movements cause an increase in the volume of the thorax.

This causes the diaphragm to flatten.

Consequently, the pressure in the thorax decreases.

The intercostal muscles contract.

Q8 When air is breathed into the lungs the ribcage moves out and the diaphragm becomes flatter. Write a paragraph describing what happens when we breathe out. In your answer include what happens to the **ribcage**, the **diaphragm**, the **volume of the thorax** and the **pressure in the thorax**.

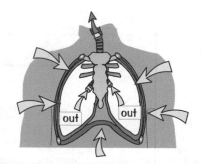

Just take a deep breath and get stuck in...

Learning how we breathe shouldn't be that difficult — it's just a case of learning the facts in the right order. The alveoli are slightly more tricky though, but you still just need to learn the facts and you'll be fine. Keep trying until you can quickly and easily answer all of these questions...

Diffusion

You're getting into some pretty exciting stuff now — that's right, here in all it's glory, diffusion.

Q1 Complete the sentences by choosing the correct word from each of the pairs below.

Diffusion is the **squashing** / **spreading** of the particles of a gas, or of any substance in solution, resulting in a net movement from a region where they are at a **higher** / **lower** concentration to a region where they are at a **higher** / **lower** concentration. This happens as a consequence of the random movement of particles.

Q2 Oxygen required for respiration passes through cell membranes and through gas exchange surfaces, such as alveoli in the lungs, by **diffusion**.

The diagram opposite shows an **alveolus** where gas exchange is taking place.

The two gases involved are **oxygen** and **carbon dioxide**. What is happening to them in the diagram?

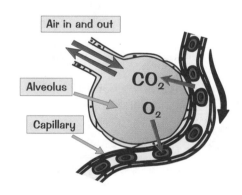

Air in and out

Alveolus

Capillary

CO_2

O_2

Q3 Oxygen is carried round the body in the form of oxyhaemoglobin. Oxygen and carbon dioxide are also exchanged at the cells in the body.

a) What happens to the **oxyhaemoglobin** carried in the red blood cells when the blood reaches body cells?

b) Carbon dioxide is a waste product of respiration. Which part of the **blood** carries carbon dioxide, and where does it carry it to?

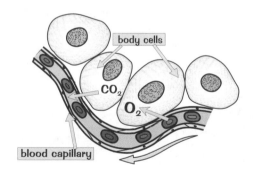

body cells

CO_2

O_2

blood capillary

Q4 The diagram to the right shows projections called **villi**. Millions of these villi cover the inside of the small intestine.

Explain how the villi **speed** up the absorption of digested food into the blood.

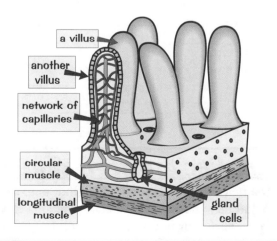

a villus

another villus

network of capillaries

circular muscle

longitudinal muscle

gland cells

The Circulatory System

The circulatory system is pretty important — it transports vital stuff all around the body.
You need to know how it does this and all the jobs that blood does for us.

Q1   There are **two** separate **circulation** systems involving the heart.

  a)   Where does each go to?
  b)   What is the main advantage of this double circulatory system?
  c)   Explain why two systems are needed.

Q2   The **circulation** system **transports** substances around the body.

  a)   Name **five** substances transported around the body by the circulation system.
  b)   There are **two** main **components** of the circulation system which maintain a **continuous flow of blood** around the body. What are they?

Q3   The **heart** pumps blood around the body.

  a)   How many **chambers** are there in the heart?
  b)   What are the **upper** chambers called? What are the **lower** chambers called?

Q4   The diagram on the right represents a cross-section of the **human heart** drawn from the front.

  a)   **Identify** each of the parts labelled 1 to 4.
  b)   **What type** of tissue is most of the **wall** of the heart made from? Explain how you could work this out from your knowledge of the **action** of the heart.
  c)   Name the four **valves** shown on the diagram.

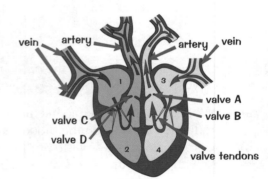

Q5   The following paragraph describes how **blood travels** through the heart.

  Use these words to fill in the spaces (a word may be used more than once):

ventricle	out	correct
contracts	atrium	valves

Blood enters an _____ of the heart. The atrium _____ and forces blood into a _____ . The _____ _____ and forces blood _____ of the heart. _____ in the heart ensure that blood flows in the _____ direction.

Cardiac Arrest — another high quality drama, I'm sure...

The heart's one of those topics that examiners just love to throw into the exam. The thing is though, if you can answer all of these questions then there's no way that they can catch you out. Make sure that you know the picture of the heart with all of the labels.

Blood Vessels

Don't sit your Exam in vain — learn this whilst you've still got the chance.

Q1   **Veins** and **arteries** do **different** jobs in the body.

Match up these **descriptions** with the correct heading:

> Carry blood at low pressure.
> Have a narrower lumen and thicker walls.
> Carry blood from the heart.
> Carry blood at high pressure.
> Have a bigger lumen and thinner walls.
> Carry blood to the heart.

Arteries

Veins

Q2   The diagrams below show **cross-sections** of arteries and veins. They are **not** drawn to scale.

a)   **Copy** the diagrams and **label** parts **A** to **D**.

b)   Describe the **similarities** and **differences** between the cross-sections of arteries and veins.

c)   **Explain** how each blood vessel is **adapted** for its function. Your correct answer to question **Q1** should help you.

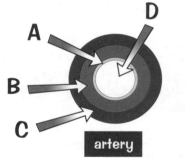 

artery   vein

Q3   The diagrams on the right show pieces of artery and vein sliced diagonally along their length. They are not drawn to scale.

a)   **Copy** the diagrams with the correct names of the blood vessels.

b)   What is the **function** of the valves in A?

c)   **Where else** in the circulatory system can these structures be found?

d)   Work out which way the blood must be flowing in vessel A and add an **arrow** to your diagram to show the **direction** of blood flow. **Explain how** you worked this out.

A

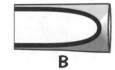

B

Q4   In the **organs**, blood flows through **blood vessels** called **capillaries**. The diagram opposite shows a picture of a **capillary**.

a)   **Label** the parts 1 - 3.

b)   **Describe** the function of the capillaries.

c)   How does their structure enable them to carry out this function effectively?

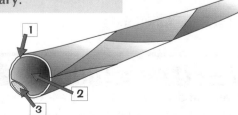

Blood

Sorry, no practical experiments to do here — it's all stuff that goes on but can't really be seen...

Q1 Draw a summary table to show the **functions** of each of the four components of blood.

Q2 **Which** of the blood cells carries oxygen as oxyhaemoglobin?

Oxygen + Haemoglobin ⟶ Oxyhaemoglobin

Q3 Fill in the spaces using the words **oxygen**, **haemoglobin**, or **oxyhaemoglobin**.

> In the lungs _____ combines with _____ to form _____ .
> In other organs, _____ splits up into _____ and _____ .

Q4 Complete this paragraph by selecting the correct word from the list below.

_____ blood cells help to protect the body against disease.
They have a _____ shape, as this lets them _____ micro-organisms.
_____ are produced to fight the _____. Bacteria produce harmful
toxins, but these are countered by _____ carried by the _____
in the blood.

micro-organisms	**antitoxins**	**plasma**
engulf	**white**	**flexible**	**antibodies**

Q5 **Plasma** is important because the red cells, platelets and white cells are suspended in it.

One other important function of plasma is transport.
Name **three substances** that plasma transports. **Choose** from the list below.

products of digestion	**hormones**	**antitoxins**	**oxygen**	**water**
urea	**dissolved mineral salts**	**carbon dioxide**	**antibodies**	

Q6 Platelets are small fragments of cells. Like red cells, they do not have a nucleus, but they are only about a third of the size of a red cell. There is approximately one platelet to every 12 red cells.

What is the **function** of platelets?

Blood — it gets right under my skin...

Blood is a nice and easy topic really — once you know the four components of blood and what each
one does you're pretty much there. Just keep practising these questions until the answers are at your
fingertips. When you've got it all just check through once more to make sure...

The Nervous System

We detect features of the world around us using our senses. Processing this information and coordinating the actions we make in response to it is a big job — and it's all done by the nervous system.

Q1 You need to know about **five** sense organs — the nose, the tongue, the ears, the eyes and the skin.

a) **Match** these **sense organs** to the following **senses** (some organs have more than one sense):

| balance | hearing | sight | smell | taste | temperature | touch |

The senses work because each sense organ contains cells that are able to detect certain stimuli. For example, the sense of balance arises from the appropriate sense organ being able to detect the position of the body.

b) Match the **senses** in part **a)** to the following **stimuli** (some stimuli may produce more than one sense).

| chemicals | light | position | sound | pressure | temperature change |

c) Draw up a **table** with the headings shown on the right. Put your answers to parts **a)** and **b)** together to complete your table. It should show which **stimuli** are detected in each sense organ, and the **sense** produced as a result.

Sense organ	Stimulus	Sense

Q2 One of the functions of the **nervous system** is to allow us to react to changes in our surroundings.

a) We respond to changes in the environment. **What** do we call these changes?
b) **What** are the **cells** called that detect these changes in the environment?
c) Suggest some **advantages** of being able to detect and respond to changes in the environment.

Q3 Look at the diagram on the right:

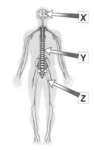

a) **Identify** the parts of the nervous system labelled **X**, **Y** and **Z**.
b) What is the **collective name** given to the parts represented by **X** and **Y**?
c) In which **direction** can nerve impulses travel in the part labelled **Y**?
d) Give **two** functions of the part labelled **X**. Is **X** involved in reflex actions?

Q4 Some responses to stimuli are **automatic** and **rapid**. These are called **reflex actions**. In a simple reflex action, electrical impulses pass along **two** different types of neurone.

Complete these sentences using the words **response**, **sensory neurone** or **motor neurone**.

a) Electrical impulses pass from a receptor along a _____ _____ to the spinal cord or brain.
b) They then pass along a _____ _____ to a muscle or gland.
c) The muscle or gland brings about the _____.

Neurones and Reflexes

Whatever you want to do in the future, you've got to know about the nervous system.
I'm serious — I really couldn't get through a day without this stuff.

Q1 Information from receptors passes along **cells** in **nerves**
to the brain, where the response is coordinated.

What are these cells called?

Q2 The two diagrams on the right show a **sensory neurone** and a motor neurone.

a) Describe what a **sensory** neurone and a **motor** neurone do.

b) Which diagram, **A** or **B**, represents a sensory neurone?
Explain how you know this.

c) **Copy** the diagrams. Add an **arrow** to each to show
the **direction** of the nerve impulse. **Label** as many
features as you can in each diagram.

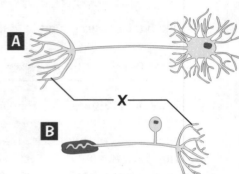

d) Each neurone is making connections with other
nerves or tissues at the part marked **X**. **Label** each
diagram to show what **X** is connected to.

e) **Explain** how the **structure** of a neurone is adapted to its function.

Q3 Copy these sentences about reflex actions, choosing
the correct word from each pair in bold:

> A reflex action is a **conscious / automatic** response to a **stimulus / receptor**. It happens
> very **quickly / slowly** and **involves / does not involve** the **brian / brain**. Reflex actions
> allow us to coordinate body activity by **remote control / nervous control**. The brain is
> only made aware of the reflex action later, so we don't do the same thing again.

Q4 If you touch a hot object with your finger, you quickly move your
finger away without having to think about it. This is a **reflex** reaction.

a) What is the **stimulus** in this reflex action?
b) What is the **response** in this reflex action?
c) What is the **effector** that makes this response happen?

Reflexes — try to answer these automatically...

Neurones and reflexes are two of the key parts of the nervous system, so you need to know and
understand them. Make an extra effort to learn how signals are transmitted, right the way
through from the stimulus to the action.

Module B02 — Control in Animals and Plants

Neurones and Reflexes

Q5   **Reflex** actions often involve **three** neurones — sensory, relay and motor, and don't always involve the brain. These sentences describe what happens in reflex actions. But to make things tricky, they've been muddled up. Write them out in the **right** order.

at a junction (synapse) between a sensory neurone and a relay neurone in the central nervous system, a chemical is released which causes an impulse to be sent along a relay neurone;

the effector is either a muscle or a gland;

impulses from a receptor pass along a sensory neurone to the central nervous system;

a muscle responds by contracting, a gland by releasing (secreting) chemical substances.

a chemical is released at the synapse between a relay neurone and a motor neurone in the central nervous system. This causes impulses to be sent along a motor neurone to the organ (the effector) which brings about the response;

Q6   This diagram represents a **reflex arc**.

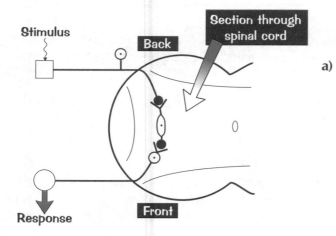

a)   Copy the diagram. Add arrows to show the direction of the **nerve impulses**. And add labels to show:

the **sensory neurone**
the **connector (relay) neurone**
the **motor neurone**
the **receptor**
the **effector**

b)   What is the role of each of the **neurones** in this reflex action?

c)   Use your answers to rearrange these features of a **reflex arc** into the correct order.

neurones (coordinator) → effector → receptor → response → stimulus

d)   Use the reflex arc to explain why reflex actions are such **fast responses**.

Q7   Describe the **reflex arcs** that take place when you are hit just below the knee-cap, and when you get a speck of grit in your eye.

The Eye

Q1   Look at the diagram on the right. It shows a section through an **eye**.

Match the names below to the parts of the eye labelled **A** to **I**. Make a **table** for your answers.

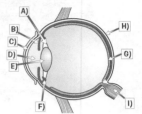

ciliary muscles   cornea   pupil

iris   retina   lens   sclera

optic nerve   suspensory ligaments

Q2   Make sure you know what all the parts of the eye do, by **matching** the part to its function:

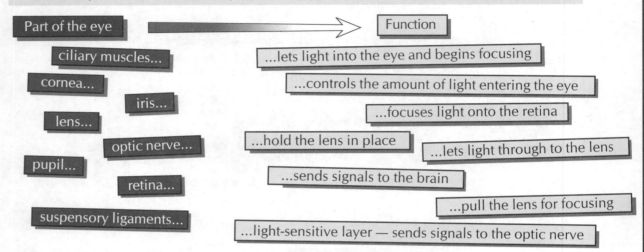

Part of the eye   ➔   Function

ciliary muscles...

cornea...

iris...

lens...

optic nerve...

pupil...

retina...

suspensory ligaments...

...lets light into the eye and begins focusing

...controls the amount of light entering the eye

...focuses light onto the retina

...hold the lens in place

...lets light through to the lens

...sends signals to the brain

...pull the lens for focusing

...light-sensitive layer — sends signals to the optic nerve

Q3   Mrs. Simpson was just settling down to watch Crownation Street when the doorbell rang. She answered the door to find a penguin on her doorstep. Despite her shock, Mrs. Simpson noticed that the penguin was wearing a blue scarf.

a)   Reflected light from the scarf entered her eyes. **Which** part of the eye does light from an object enter?

b)   What do the **cornea** and **lens** then do?

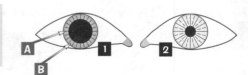

c)   The retina contains the receptor cells which are sensitive to light.
How does information get from the **retina** to the **brain**?

d)   After a moment's thought, Mrs. Simpson decided to take a closer look at the penguin.
To focus on near objects, the lens needs to become fat so that light can be bent onto the retina.
Explain the roles of the **ciliary muscles** and **suspensory ligaments** in changing the shape of the lens.

Q4   The iris contains **circular** and **radial** muscles. These muscles control the diameter of the pupil. The diagrams on the right show the iris in two different light conditions.

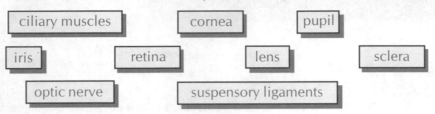

a)   What is the **black circle** in the centre?

b)   **Identify** the two muscle types, **A** and **B**.

c)   Which diagram, **1** or **2**, shows the eye in **bright** light? **Explain** why you chose this diagram.

d)   In diagram **1**, which type of muscle is **relaxed** and which is **contracted**?

e)   In diagram **2**, which type of muscle is **relaxed** and which is **contracted**?

f)   Use your answers so far to **explain** how the iris controls the amount of light entering the eye.

g)   What **other muscles** are in the eye? What is their **function**?

Module BD2 — Control in Animals and Plants

Hormones

Q1   **Complete** this table and **label** the endocrine glands shown on the picture.

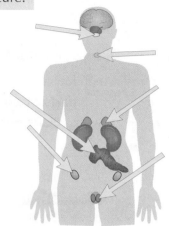

Name of hormone	Gland	Function
a) Insulin		Stimulates glycogen formation from glucose
b) Oestrogen, progesterone		develops female sexual characteristics
c) Follicle Stimulating Hormone (FSH)		causes eggs to mature and ovaries to produce oestrogen
d)	Pituitary	
e)		controls the metabolism
f)	Adrenal	
g) Testosterone		

You wouldn't actually get testes and ovaries in the same body. You knew that anyway, though.

Q2   Adrenaline is produced to prepare the body for a fight or flight situation. Pick the correct words to complete the sentences below.

Adrenaline is secreted by the **pituitary** / **adrenal** gland. This happens to prepare the body for fighting or running away from a dangerous situation. Your breathing and heart rate **increase** / **decrease**, and blood is also diverted **away from** / **towards** the muscles from the skin, which makes the skin look pale. Glucose is released by the **liver** / **pancreas** to increase the sugar level of the blood, body hairs stand on end and you start to sweat.

Q3   Secondary sexual characteristics are produced by testosterone in males, and oestrogen in females. **Complete** the table below with five secondary sexual characteristics for both males and females.

Males	Females

Q4   The bloodstream is the method of transport that carries hormones to their target organ.

Using the labels below, **copy and complete** the diagram opposite showing the production and action of hormones in the body.

endocrine gland

response

target organ

bloodstream

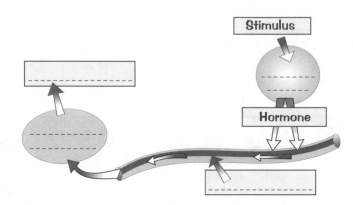

Hormones

Q5 Describe a problem a diabetic person could face when their blood sugar level becomes too high.

Q6 **Diabetes** is a disease in which a person's blood sugar may rise to a level that can be fatal.

a) Which **hormone** do diabetics produce too little of?

b) Which **part** of the body produces this hormone?

c) How can diabetes be **treated**?

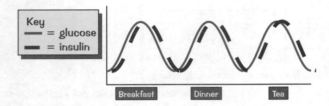

This graph shows blood sugar and insulin levels of a diabetic person having three meals and three insulin injections a day.

d) Draw a graph to show what would happen if the diabetic **forgot** to take an insulin injection at tea time. Explain the shape of your graph.

Q7 The **blood glucose concentration** of the body is monitored and controlled by the **pancreas**.

What does the pancreas do when the blood glucose concentration is too **high**?
How does this affect the **liver**?

Q8 The hormones and treatments below are given by doctors to control various body functions. Match each with the correct description.

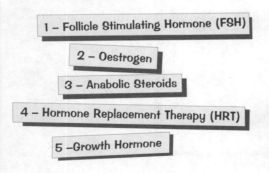

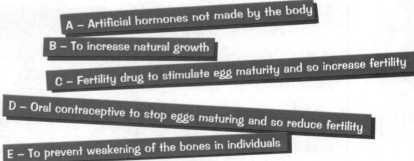

Q9 Glenn Johnson, the Solihull runner, took anabolic steroids to improve his athletic performance. How do anabolic steroids **improve** your performance?

Hormones — the best way to brighten up your day...

Hormonal diseases are quite simple — as long as you remember the disease and the hormone which is used to treat it, you'll be fine. Definitely practise the questions on diabetes and insulin until you've got it all firmly implanted in your head. Just keep trying...

<u>Hormones</u>

Dead important stuff to know if you're a woman, and, well,
dead important stuff to know if you're a man...

Q10   "The combined Pill" is a contraceptive taken by women that works by controlling egg production.

a)   Which **two** hormones does the pill contain?

b)   What do you think the **effect** of taking the pill **regularly**
would be on the level of oestrogen in the body?

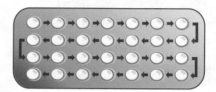

Maintaining oestrogen at this level inhibits production of FSH.

c)   After a period of time, **what effect** would this have on **egg production**?

d)   Would you expect the egg production of someone on the pill to **return to normal**
after they stopped taking it? **Why**?

Q11   Oestrogen and progesterone control menstruation.

a)   **Name the place** where they are produced.

b)   **Copy the diagram** on the right and indicate where these
hormones are produced.

Q12   Women's fertility can be altered with the introduction of particular hormones.

a)   Which hormone would be given to **increase** the fertility of a woman with low fertility?

b)   **Explain** how this hormone has the required effect.

Q13   Match each of the hormones in the grey boxes on the left with their matching descriptions.

Oestrogen

Progesterone

Stops production of FSH, causes the
lining of the uterus to thicken and
the release of an egg on day 14.

Maintains the lining of the uterus.
When the level of progesterone
falls, the lining breaks down.

Hormones

Hormones helped us all to get where we are today, and if you can answer these questions they'll help you to get to where you want to go — sailing through the exam...

Q14 The diagram below shows what happens at different stages of the **menstrual cycle** and during **pregnancy**.

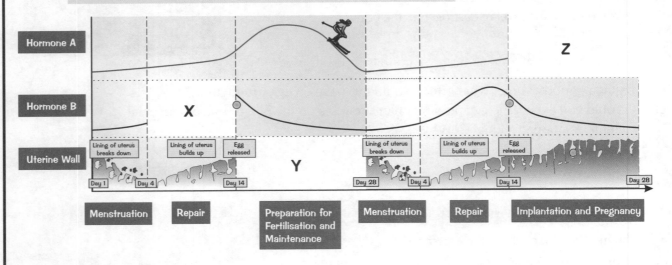

a) **Name** hormones **A** and **B**.

b) Three sections of the diagram (**X**, **Y** and **Z**) have been left incomplete. **Draw** what you would expect to see.

c) **Which hormone**, not shown above, **stimulates oestrogen production**?

Q15 With the help of the diagram above, answer the following questions:

a) Name the **hormone** that brings about the **repair and thickening** of the uterus lining.

b) Name the **hormone** that **maintains** the uterus lining and prepares the body for pregnancy.

Q16 Fertility treatment can be used by couples who are having problems conceiving. Part of this treatment can involve stimulating egg production.

a) Which hormone would be taken to stimulate **egg development**?

b) Which hormone is then produced by the ovaries to stimulate **egg release**?

c) Give **one** example of a problem with this treatment.

Pro-jest-erone — the joke promoting hormone....

The menstrual cycle can be pretty tricky — but you've got to know about it. For each hormone you need to know <u>what controls it</u> and <u>what it controls</u>. Draw a graph of all the hormone levels. It'll help you get it all straight in your brain — and it's the sort of graph that tends to appear in the Exams.

Plant Hormones

Q1 **Auxins** are **hormones** which control growth in plants. They move through the plant in solution. A young broad bean seedling was placed in the ground sideways.

a)   **i)** In **which direction** does the **root** grow?
     ii) **What causes** the root to grow in this direction?
     iii) **What stimuli** affect the direction of root growth?

b)   **i)** **Which way** does the **shoot** grow?
     ii) **Why does** the shoot grow in this direction?
     iii) **What stimuli** affect the direction of shoot growth?

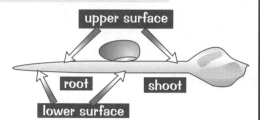

Q2 Tony decided that he was going to grow the straightest corn shoots possible.

a) What could he do to corn seedlings to make them grow **straight**?

Two weeks after growing the seedlings, Tony noticed that the shoots were growing to the **left**.

b) Give a possible reason for this.
Explain how Tony could **make** the seedlings grow straight again.

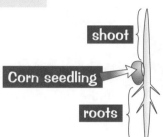

Q3 The diagram shows four boxes. Each of the boxes is placed in the **same** uniform environment, and has one cress plant placed inside it.

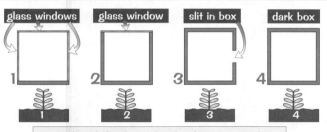

| glass windows | glass window | slit in box | dark box |

1   2   3   4

Cress plants before being placed in their respective boxes

a) **Redraw** the boxes. In each one, show the **appearance** of the cress plant after a few days.

b) For each box **explain** the pattern of growth you've drawn.

Q4 In his spare time, Mr. Tomavitch likes nothing better than to tend to his tomatoes. In fact, he has made a small fortune from selling his high quality tomatoes around the world. Using your knowledge of plant hormones, suggest how and why Mr. Tomavitch might do the following:

a) **Reproduce** large numbers of tomato plants quickly.

b) **Regulate** the ripening of his tomatoes.

Q5 Complete the boxes in the table.

Chemical Involved	How is it used?	What effect does it have?
Rooting hormone		
	Sprayed over broad-leaved weed plants	
Growth regulator	Applied to flower buds	

Population and Habitat

Plants and animals can live in very inhospitable environments,
but to survive they have to adapt to their surroundings...

Q1 Explain the following **collecting methods**, using diagrams where necessary:

a) Pooters.
b) Nets.
c) Pit-fall traps.
d) Quadrats.

Q2 Estimate the total population of a 550m² field if a 1m² quadrat within the field
contains 110 grass plants, 40 buttercups, 15 clovers, 10 daisies and 4 stag beetles.

This estimate may not be very accurate. State **two** things you could do to make it **more accurate**?

Q3 What do the words **predator** and **prey** mean? Give two examples of a predator and its prey.

Q4 Draw a table with the headings shown on the right.

In the '**factor**' column, list the things that can affect the
size of a population of organisms. In the '**examples**'
column, give an example of this factor at work.
One line has been done for you as an example.
(Think of plant examples as well as animal examples.)

Factor	Examples
Competition for water	Weeds and wheat

Q5 The sidewinder is a snake which lives in deserts. It moves sideways across
the sand by throwing its body into a series of S-shapes, always keeping a
loop of the S-shape off the ground, with two other parts touching.

Explain why it does this.

Q6 Many desert animals, such as the kangaroo rat, spend the day in a burrow and come out at night.

What are the **advantages** and **disadvantages** of doing this?

Q7 Desert plants are adapted to survive in their environment.

Study each of these features carefully. For each feature, decide what **condition** in the environment
the plant has adapted to, and **explain** how the adaptation helps the plant to survive in the desert.

a) The seeds of flowering desert plants can lie dormant in the soil for years
until the rain allows them to germinate, grow and flower quickly.
b) Some plants have long roots which reach deep underground.
c) Some plants have shallow roots which spread just under the surface.
d) Succulent plants store water in their leaves, stems and roots.
e) Some plants drop their leaves during a dry spell.
They usually have small leaves.
f) Some plants take in and store carbon dioxide at night.
During the day their stomata are closed.
g) Many plants have modified leaves which form thorns,
and photosynthesis occurs in the stems.

Q8 Lemmings are small rodents that live in the tundra. They have a rounded body about 12cm long.
Their fur is light brown, and they have small ears that are hidden by fur. Lemmings live in burrows.

Explain how the lemming is adapted to life in the Arctic tundra.

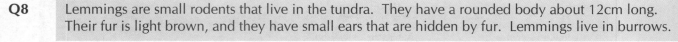

Population and Habitat

Q1 The graph below shows the average daytime temperature (line) and rainfall (bars) in the Arctic. The temperature can fall to –80°C and the wind can blow at over 300 km/h.
It's dark all the time in winter, but in the summer the sun never sets.

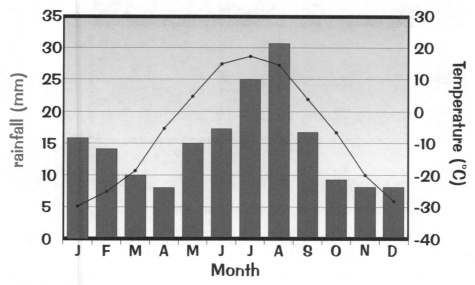

a) From this information, **suggest** what the environment is like in the Arctic.

b) It's not all sea and ice in the Arctic. There is a lot of barren land too, known as the tundra. The plants there often grow very close to the ground, and have small leaves.
Suggest a **reason** why the plants grow in this way.

c) **What problems** will animals face living in the Arctic?
Suggest some adaptations that would allow animals to live successfully in the Arctic.

Q2 The camel lives in the desert — a dry, hot environment.
To help it survive, it is **adapted** to its environment in several ways.

Explain how each of the features below helps the camel survive in the desert.

a) It has a large surface area.

b) It can drink up to 20 gallons of water at once and store it easily.

c) It produces little urine and even less sweat.

d) It is a sandy colour.

e) It has large feet.

f) It has a hump where it stores all its fat, so there is no layer of body fat.

g) It can tolerate big changes in its body temperature.

Q3 Just like the camel has adapted to life in the desert, the lion has adapted to being a predator. List **three** features of the lion that make it a good predator.

Q4 List **three physical** factors which may affect an organism's ability to live, grow and reproduce.

Population and Habitat

Q1   Organisms compete with one another for essential resouces.
Copy and complete the table to show what things they compete for.
(Hint — two of these are the same for both plants and animals.)

Plants	Animals
1)	1)
2)	2)
3)	3)

Q2   Answer the following questions about how rabbits are adapted to avoid predators.

a)   Describe how the way a rabbit moves helps it survive.

b)   How does the colour of the rabbit's fur help it to avoid capture?

c)   Rabbits' eyes are on either side of their head.
How does this help them spot predators?

d)   Why does the rabbit have big ears?

e)   How does a rabbit's tail alert other rabbits of danger?

Q3   Complete the following paragraph about the polar bear using
the words from the box. Each word can be used only once.

white	insulation	reduces	prey
thick	sheds	prevent	minimum
powerful	camouflage	runner	

The polar bear's surface area is kept to a _____
compared to its body weight. This _____ heat loss.
It has a _____ layer of blubber for _____ . Its fur is
greasy so it _____ water after swimming to _____
cooling due to evaporation. It has _____ fur for _____
and is a _____ _____ which helps it catch _____ on land.

Who you
calling blubbery?

A bear adapted to 4000° C? — must be a solar bear.

There are more animals out there than polar bears and rabbits. The point here is to <u>get used</u> to
thinking about <u>what makes animals well adapted</u>. Things like size, fur colour and speed of
movement are <u>general principles</u> and can be applied to <u>any animal</u> they throw at you in the Exam.

Food Chains and Pyramids

Food chains and pyramids. What does fast-food have to do with
the ancient Egyptians and how does that come into GCSE Science...

Q1   Describe a **mutualistic** relationship using root nodules in leguminous plants as an example.

Q2   **Connect** these food chains to form a food web for these woodland plants and animals.

trees → butterfly → robin → sparrowhawk

trees → aphids → ladybird → robin

trees → mouse → owl

grass → mouse → owl

grass → rabbit → owl

Q3   Pyramids of number are useful for displaying information.

a)   What **information** does a pyramid of numbers give?

b)   In the food chain, carrot → rabbit → fox, **which row** in the table on the right represents the most likely numbers of each organism?

c)   What do you notice about the **size** of the organism as you look from left to right along this food chain?

d)   Which pyramid of numbers below most closely matches the correct answer to part **b)**?

	Carrots	Rabbits	Foxes
A	1	100	4000
B	1	4000	100
C	100	1	4000
D	100	4000	1
E	4000	1	100
F	4000	100	1

e)   What do you notice about the size of the organism and the width of its bar on the pyramid of numbers in the correct answer to part **d)**?

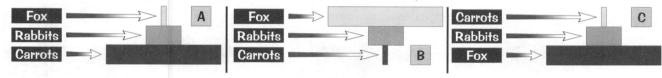

Q4   **Draw** pyramids of numbers for the food chains in **a)** and **b)**. Make sure you **label** each step with the name of the organism and how many of them there are.

a)   Microscopic water plants (1 million) → water fleas (100,000) → trout (50) → kingfisher (1)

b)   Oak tree (1) → caterpillars (500) → birds (5)

c)   Ideally, the width of each bar would be drawn to scale, so that the trout bar in part **a)** would be fifty times wider than the kingfisher bar. This is usually not possible. **Explain why**.

d)   If you have done part **b)** correctly, it will not look very pyramid-shaped. **Why** can a pyramid of numbers have an unusual shape like this?

e)   **Draw** a pyramid to show the following short food chain: wheat → human. **Decide** on a suitable width for the wheat bar.

f)   In tropical countries, a disease called schistosomiasis can be a big problem. It's caused by a parasitic worm, about 1cm long, which lives in the blood vessels and feeds on blood. A person might be infected by dozens of these worms. **Add** a labelled bar for the worm to your pyramid of numbers. **Explain why** this pyramid is not pyramid-shaped.

g)   Think of another food chain that will produce a pyramid of numbers that is **not** pyramid-shaped. **Draw** and **label** the pyramid, and write down the food chain alongside it. **Explain** why your pyramid has its unusual shape.

Module BD3— Ecology

Food Chains and Pyramids

Q1   Explain what is meant by the word **biomass**.
What information does a pyramid of biomass give?

Q2   One of the food chains in the North Sea is: **phytoplankton → zooplankton → small fish → cod**

The biomass of each of the organisms in the food chain was estimated from samples and experiments. It was found that for every 1kg of cod, there were 100kg of phytoplankton, 80kg of zooplankton and 10kg of small fish. In each case, the masses are dry masses.

a)   **Draw** a pyramid of biomass for this food chain. Draw it **to scale**, and make sure that you label each bar with the name of the organism and its biomass in kg.

b)   In some pyramids of numbers and biomass, the top bar can be shown as a vertical line. **Explain** why this is sometimes necessary.

c)   Between which two organisms in this food chain is the **most** mass lost? **How much** mass is lost?

d)   Between which two organisms in this food chain is the **greatest proportion** of mass lost?

e)   Suggest reasons why the biomass is **less** at each level than the one before it.

f)   The wet mass of a small fish averages about 1.5kg, and that of adult cod averages about 7.5kg. Assuming that both types of fish have the same proportion of water in their bodies, **how many** small fish feed one cod?

Q3   Look at these pyramids:

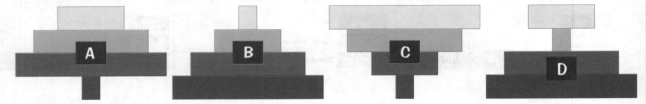

Choose one of the pyramids above to **match** each fo the following descriptions.
You can use each pyramid once, more than once, or not at all.

a)   The pyramid of numbers for a community that relies on a large producer.
b)   The pyramid of biomass for a woodland community.
c)   The pyramid of numbers for a food chain that ends with parasites such as fleas.
d)   The pyramid of numbers for a marine community in which the producers are tiny algae.

Q4   Fill in the blanks in the following paragraph, using the words in the box.

> The mass of living material at each stage in a food chain is
> _____ than it was at the stage below. This means
> pyramids of _____ get _____ the higher you go.
> This is not always the case with pyramids of _____.

numbers
less
narrower
biomass

It's a cod eat small fish eat zooplankton world out there...

Remember it takes <u>a lot</u> of food from the level below to keep one animal alive. <u>Pyramids of biomass</u> always get narrower the higher you go, but <u>pyramids of numbers</u> can be any shape — all the fleas on one mangy dog still weigh less than the dog itself. (Unless it's got them *really really* bad...)

Food Chains and Pyramids

Q1   Algae → slugs → frogs → heron ...is an example of a food chain found in a pond.

For every heron, there are 80 kg of frogs, and for every kg of frogs there are 20 kg of algae. If there are 400 kg of frogs in the lake how many herons are there?
How much algae is there?

Q2   Answer these questions about how **energy** is transferred through **food chains**:

a)   What sort of organism is always at the **start** of any food chain?
b)   How does this sort of organism bring **energy** into the chain?
c)   What happens to the **amount of energy** and **material** present as you move up a food chain?

Q3   Farmer Giles likes to be efficient. He wants to produce as much food as possible from his land.

He has two options:
1)   Use the land for grazing cattle and sheep.
2)   Grow vegetables, wheat and other crops that can be eaten by humans.

Which option should he choose for **maximum efficiency**? **Explain** your answer.

Q4   Energy and material are lost at each stage in a food chain. It doesn't disappear – it's used up.

a)   **Explain** how energy and material are lost at each stage in a food chain.
b)   Use the words in the box to fill in the blanks.

> Much of the energy loss in _____ occurs as _____ loss to the environment. This loss is _____ high in mammals and birds. Their bodies must be kept at a _____ temperature which is usually _____ than that of their environment.

| higher |
| very |
| heat |
| respiration |
| constant |

c)   Explain why a pet goldfish requires much **less** food than a pet gerbil.
Bear in mind the last bit of part b.
d)   Suppose that a cow gets 250 kJ of energy from eating some grass, uses 75 kJ for respiration and loses 150 kJ through excretion. What **percentage** of the energy is **retained** by the cow?

Q5   Like any business, the efficiency of food production is very important.

a)   Battery farmed chickens have their **ability to move restricted** and they are kept in conditions close to their own body temperature.
How does this method of farming increase the **efficiency** of **food production**?
b)   Describe how **hormones** are used to increase the efficiency of **fruit growing**.
c)   What are the **advantages** and **disadvantages** of these two methods of food production?

All this eating is tiring me out...

Energy and material are lost at each stage in a food chain. So the efficiency of food production can be improved by reducing the number of stages in food chains. You can also minimise the energy loss at each stage, but this can have some disadvantages. For us that is, not to mention the poor chickens.

Decomposition

Q1 Material is constantly being removed from, and returned to the environment.

  a) **Why** do living things **remove materials** from the environment?

  b) **How** are the materials **returned** to the environment?

  c) **Why** is it **important** that the materials are returned?

Q2 Bacteria and fungi can break down solid waste materials from animals.

They can also break down materials in dead animals and plants.
This is known as decomposition or decay.

  a) **What general word** is used to describe bacteria and fungi that break down **dead** material?

  b) **What is the benefit** to the bacteria and fungi of **digesting** these materials?

  c) **What carbon compound** will be returned to the atmosphere as a result of their activities?

  d) **What substances** will they release into the soil?

  e) **Why** are bacteria and fungi important for the **recycling** of carbon in the carbon cycle?

Q3 Microorganisms digest materials best under certain conditions.

In each of the following statements about the conditions,
pick the correct word from each pair.

  a) Microorganisms digest material faster in **warm** / **cold** conditions.

  b) They digest faster if the conditions are **dry** / **moist** .

  c) Many microorganisms are also more active if there is **plenty of** / **not a lot of** oxygen.

Q4 Humans sometimes use microorganisms to decompose materials.

  a) **Why** are decomposing microorganisms **added** to waste at a sewage works?

  b) **Why** must the waste in a compost heap be **exposed to air**?

  c) **How** do plants **benefit** from having compost added to the soil?

Q5 For a **stable** community of organisms, processes which remove substances
from the environment should be balanced with which other processes?

What a rotten page this is...

Yep, it's literally a load of rubbish. Make sure you know the role of <u>bacteria</u> and <u>fungi</u> in <u>rotting down</u> waste animal and plant material. Keep on trying these questions until you get them right.

The Carbon Cycle

The <u>Carbon Cycle</u> describes how carbon is removed from the environment, used by plants and animals and then returned to the environment. The <u>Spin Cycle</u> removes water from your clothes.

Q1   Green plants remove carbon from the environment.

a)   What process in plants removes carbon dioxide from the atmosphere?

b)   What process in plants returns some of this carbon dioxide to the atmosphere?

c)   Copy and complete the diagram opposite using the words below. **Light** boxes are spaces for substances. **Dark** ones are spaces for processes.

| photosynthesis | carbon dioxide |
| respiration | carbon |

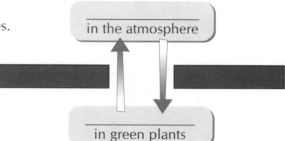

in the atmosphere

in green plants

d)   What three products do plants make with the **carbon** from carbon dioxide?

Q2   Animals also need carbon to survive — they get it by eating green plants.

a)   What happens to the carbon present in plants when they are eaten by animals?

b)   What process in animals returns carbon dioxide to the atmosphere?

Q3   Explain how the carbon present in dead plant and animal material is returned to the atmosphere.

Q4   Fill in the blanks in the paragraph about the carbon cycle below, using the words in the box.

fats	microorganisms	dioxide	carbohydrates
respire	carbon	eating	proteins
respiration	green	decomposed	

_____ _____ is removed from the atmosphere by _____ plants for photosynthesis. Some is returned by _____ . The carbon is used to make _____ , _____ and _____ which make up the body of the plants. Animals get carbon by _____ plants, and return some carbon dioxide to the atmosphere when they respire. Dead plant and animal material is _____ by _____ . More carbon dioxide is returned to the environment when they _____ .

The Nitrogen Cycle

It's no surprise that the Nitrogen Cycle tells us about the constant cycling of nitrogen in the environment.
It's a bit more complicated than the Carbon Cycle, though — make sure you can do all these questions.

The Nitrogen Cycle

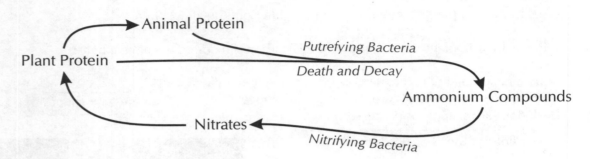

Q1   As in the carbon cycle, it's green plants that **remove** nitrogen from the environment.

a)   How do green plants get nitrogen from the environment?

b)   What do the plants need nitrogen for?

c)   Why do animals need nitrogen?

d)   How do animals get the nitrogen that they need?

Q2   Nitrogen is **returned** to the environment
when plant and animal material decomposes.

a)   What sort of bacteria break down animal waste and dead
plant and animal material?

b)   What is produced by this process?

c)   Explain how the product is converted to nitrates in the soil.

Q3   What happens to the **energy** present in the nitrates originally absorbed by the plants?

Q4   **Label** the following statements true or false.

a)   Green plants absorb nitrogen from the air around them.

b)   Plants and animals return nitrogen to the atmosphere when they respire.

c)   Green plants absorb nitrates from the soil.

d)   Animals get nitrogen by eating green plants.

e)   Plants and animals need nitrogen to make fats in their bodies.

f)   Nitrifying bacteria convert animal waste and dead plant
and animal material into ammonium compounds.

g)   Nitrifying bacteria convert ammonium compounds to nitrates.

h)   Animals can absorb nitrogen directly from the air.

The Carbon and Nitrogen Cycles

Q1 Complete this diagram of the **nitrogen cycle**, using the labels on the right.

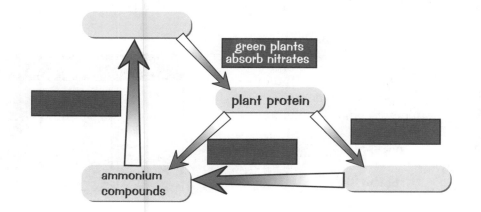

animal protein

nitrifying bacteria

death and decay

nitrates in soil

animals eat plants

Q2 Draw up a table like the one shown on the right. Complete your table to show the processes that convert **nitrates** in the soil to **ammonium compounds**, and those that convert ammonium compounds back to nitrates in the soil.

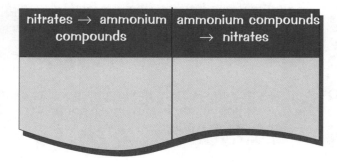

nitrates → ammonium compounds	ammonium compounds → nitrates

Q3 Here's a quick test to see if you really know everything about the Carbon Cycle and the Nitrogen Cycle. Go on, you know you want to.

a) Name **two** places where humans use **decomposing** microorganisms.

b) Will materials decompose quicker in cold or warm temperatures?

c) Name **two** sorts of material in plants that are made from carbon.

d) Which **process** in green plants **removes carbon dioxide** from the atmosphere?

e) How does the **decomposition** of plant and animal material replace carbon dioxide in the atmosphere?

f) What sort of **bacteria** convert ammonium compounds to nitrates in the soil?

g) What sort of chemical in plants and animals requires nitrogen?

Our Effect on the Environment

For a supposedly intelligent species, humans have done some pretty dumb stuff to this planet. It's no wonder none of the animals will talk to us...

Q1 With so many people in the world, we take up a lot of the room. **List four** ways that humans reduce the amount of land available for other animals and plants.

Q2 For each of the following **pollutants** produced by the human race, decide whether they affect air, land or water and put them in the appropriate column. Some pollutants may fit in more than one column.

air	land	water

sulphur dioxide   pesticides   nitrogen oxides

sewage

carbon dioxide   herbicides   fertiliser

Q3 Mr McDoodah owns a highly successful global fast food business. There is such demand for his burgers and hot dogs that he needs **more land** to farm his cows. He decides to buy some land in the Amazon rainforest, cut down the trees and graze cattle on it.

In what **three** ways will his actions increase the amount of greenhouse gases in the atmosphere?

Q4 As you can see from the graph opposite, the world population is growing exponentially. **Answer** these questions about how this affects the environment.

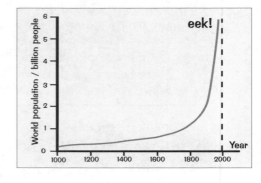

   a) **How** does this affect the rate of use of raw materials?

   b) **What** could this mean for supplies of non-renewable energy sources such as coal, oil and gas?

   c) Are the effects of human activity **larger** or **smaller** than they were 200 years ago?

   d) **Explain** why the proper handling of waste has never been more important than it is now.

Q5 Most of the world's energy is produced by **burning fossil fuels** such as coal, oil and natural gas. This method of energy production has several environmental drawbacks.

   a) **Name** the greenhouse gas produced by burning fossil fuels.

   b) **Why** has large scale deforestation increased the amount of this gas in the atmosphere?

   c) Some fossil fuels contain sulphur or nitrogen impurities.

     Explain why burning these fuels produces **acid rain**.

   d) Suggest **another reason** why being over-reliant on fossil fuels is not a good idea.

Q6 Answer these questions about **environmental impact**.

   a) Which uses the **most resources** and creates the **most pollution**: the **developed world** or the **developing world**?

   b) Which has the largest proportion of the world's **population**: the **developed world** or the **developing world**?

Pollution

Q1   The Examiners' favourite phrase this year is "**sustainable development**".

a)   **What** is **sustainable development**? (Proper definition please.)

b)   **Why** is it important?

c)   **Explain sustainable development** in terms of woodland and fish stocks.

d)   **Which** aspects of the ecosystems need to be monitored carefully to sustain development?

Q2   The efficiency of farming has been greatly increased by the introduction of chemicals such as fertilisers and by the use of intensive farming.

a)   How do fertilisers aid the growth of crops?

b)   A farmer accidentally sprays his field next to a river with **too much fertiliser**. It rains soon after he finishes. What will happen to the excess fertiliser?

c)   What is the **name** of the damage fertilisers cause to lakes and rivers? (Make sure you spell it correctly.)

Q3   The sentences below are about a lake becoming polluted with fertilisers. They are muddled up.

a)   Rewrite them in the correct order.

> - Fish and other aquatic animals die because of a lack of oxygen.
> - The microbes take more oxygen from the water for their respiration.
> - Excess fertilisers leach from the soil and are washed into the lake.
> - The number of microbes that feed on dead organisms increases.
> - There is increased competition between the plants, and some die as a result.
> - Water plants in the lake start to grow rapidly.

b)   In the corrected sequence, **why** should water plants grow **more quickly**?

c)   **What resources** are the water plants **competing** for? **Which resource** is probably in excess?

d)   If there are more plants in the lake, you might expect more oxygen to be produced by photosynthesis. **Why** does the oxygen content of the water go **down** instead?

e)   Normally, the action of decomposers such as bacteria is welcomed. It allows scarce nutrients to be recycled so other organisms in the community can use them (eg: in the nitrogen cycle). **Why** is the action of decomposers such a **problem** in the case of a eutrophic lake?

Q4   Biological control is an environmentally friendly alternative to pesticides.

a)   **How** does biological control work?

b)   Give **two advantages** and **two disadvantages** of biological control.

Q5   Animals such as the red kite, the red squirrel and the osprey are **endangered** animals in Britain.

a)   **Why** are these species dying out?

b)   **How** can these species be protected?

c)   **How** would **sustainable development** help to save these species?

Chemical Equations

Q1 Consider the following **formulae** and answer the questions below.

$$NaCl \qquad MgCO_3 \qquad H_2 \qquad KOH \qquad Ca(OH)_2$$

a) For each substance, state the **number** of atoms of each **element** in one molecule.

b) Decide which of the substances are **elements** and which are **compounds**.

c) State the **total** number of atoms in one molecule of each.

d) **Name** the substances.

Q2 **Write out** the following symbol equations in **words** (they are **not balanced**).

a) $CaCO_3 \rightarrow CaO + CO_2$

b) $MgO + HCl_{(aq)} \rightarrow MgCl_2 + H_2O$

c) $SO_2 + O_2 \rightarrow SO_3$

d) $Na_2CO_3 + HNO_{3(aq)} \rightarrow NaNO_3 + H_2O + CO_2$

e) $N_2 + H_2 \rightarrow NH_3$

Q3 **Balance** the **symbol equations** in the question above.

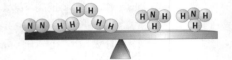

Q4 Use the **table** below to answer the questions:

Reactants		Products	
Mg	O_2	MgO	
Na	Cl_2	NaCl	
Ca	Cl_2	$CaCl_2$	
Na	H_2O	NaOH	H_2
KNO_3		KNO_2	O_2

a) For each reaction, write down the **total number** of atoms in one particle of each of:

(i) the reactants

(ii) the products

b) Use part **a)** to help you write a **balanced** symbol equation for each reaction.

Top Tips: Learning how to balance equations is really important. It might seem hard at first but keep practising... it will get easier. Remember — just keep chasing unbalanced elements and it will sort itself out... eventually.

Rates of Reaction

Not all reactions happen at the same rate.
Not a lot of people know that.

Q1 Place these chemical reactions **in order** of their speed, starting with the fastest reaction:

| Frying an egg | Striking a match | A car rusting | Concrete setting | Digesting food |

Q2 Which of the statements below are **true** and which are **false**?

	True	False
Catalysts are used up in reactions		
Catalysts are specific to certain reactions		
Enzymes are biological catalysts		
Reactions slow if catalysts are used		
Enzymes increase the activation energy		

	True	False
Reactions will speed up if they are heated		
Usually only small quantities of catalyst are needed		
Increasing concentration increases the rate of reaction		
Pressure increases the rates of gaseous reactions		
Reactions are fast initially, then slow down		

Q3 The following changes may speed up the rate of a chemical reaction between an **acid** and **magnesium**.

Put a tick in the box next to each one that will **SPEED UP** the reaction (assume that there is initially an excess of acid).

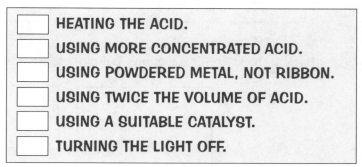

- [ ] HEATING THE ACID.
- [ ] USING MORE CONCENTRATED ACID.
- [ ] USING POWDERED METAL, NOT RIBBON.
- [ ] USING TWICE THE VOLUME OF ACID.
- [ ] USING A SUITABLE CATALYST.
- [ ] TURNING THE LIGHT OFF.

Q4 **Describe** a simple reaction that could be studied by monitoring the rate at which the **product** is formed.

Q5 Reactions can be monitored by looking at how the mass of reactants decreases. **Describe** a simple reaction that could be studied in this manner.

Q6 Reacting particles don't always collide **properly** or **effectively**. Sometimes they miss or collide as shown on the right.

Complete the diagram to show what might be happening to the particles in each case.

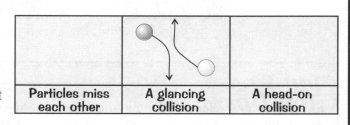

| Particles miss each other | A glancing collision | A head-on collision |

Rates of Reaction

Q1   Products are produced at a rate shown by a **rate curve**.

a)   Copy the graph opposite then draw a **typical rate curve**.

| Fast |
| Slowing |
| Stopped |

b)   Add the labels on the right to the curve you've drawn.

Products / *Time*

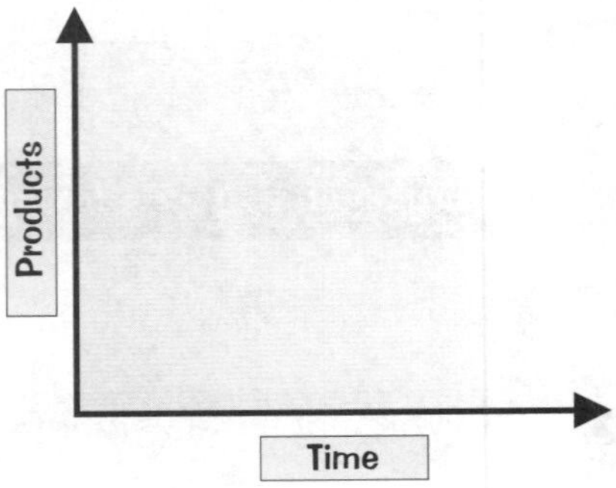

c)   For a reaction to occur, reacting particles must bump into each other with enough energy.

Imagine a reaction where two chemicals ⬤ and ⬤ collide to react.

The product would be ⬤⬤

The reaction would therefore be: ⬤ + ⬤ ⟶ ⬤⬤

Look at the stages of a reaction below — these ones, just here...

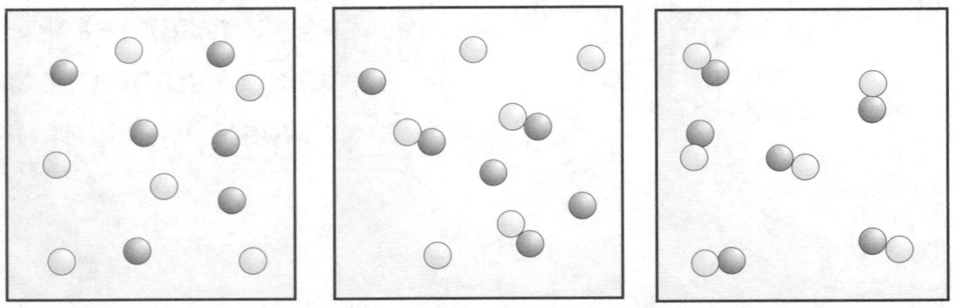

| Reaction | | | |
| Speed | | | |

Complete the diagrams by placing the labels below under the correct pictures.

END   **MIDDLE**   **START**

STOPPED   **SLOWING**   **FAST**

Top Tips   Measuring the rate at which the <u>products</u> are formed is just one way of <u>monitoring</u> the <u>rate</u> of a reaction. Make sure you can <u>explain</u> this method and draw a <u>graph</u> of the amount of product formed against time. You also need to remember the <u>four</u> things that affect the rate of a reaction — <u>temperature</u>, <u>concentration</u>, <u>surface area</u> and <u>catalysts</u>.

Module CD1 — Equations and Rates of Reaction

Rates of Reaction

Q1 An experiment can be carried out to investigate the effect of changing the temperature on the rate of reaction. The graph below shows results from such an experiment. The acid is increasingly warmer in experiments 1, 2 and 3 .

a) What **simple conclusion** about the rate of reaction can you draw from these graphs?

b) For each graph, **calculate** the rate over the first 10 seconds.

c) What do you notice about the **change in the rate** of the reaction for an increase of 10°C?

d) Does the **temperature** affect the amount of **product** formed?

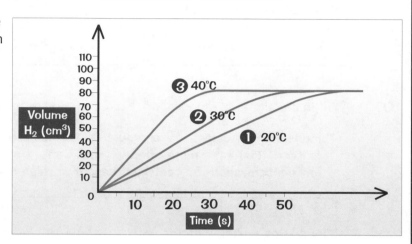

Q2 The apparatus below may be used to investigate the reaction between marble chips and dilute hydrochloric acid. Some marble chips are left unreacted at the end.

A graph showing the results from such an experiment is shown on the right.

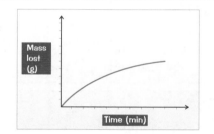

Here are four other graphs plotted to the same scale:

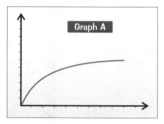
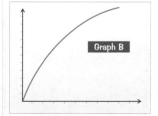
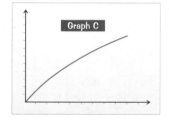
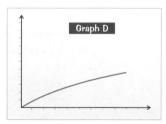

a) Referring to the original graph, **match each** of the graphs **A-D** with the correct description:

i) the same volume of acid but twice as concentrated.

ii) the same concentration of acid but twice the volume.

iii) the same mass of marble chips but smaller chips.

iv) the same volume and concentration of ice-cold acid.

b) Use the theory of collisions to explain each of your answers to part **a)**.

Collision Theory

Q1 **Fill in** the blanks below, using each word once.

energy   collide   catalyst   concentration   collision theory

Particles can only react if they _____ with enough _____ for the reaction to take place. This is called the _____ _____. There are four factors that can change the rate of a reaction: temperature, _____, surface area and the use of a suitable _____.

Q2 **Fill in** the blanks in the text and diagrams below using each word once or not at all.

moderate   faster   energy   surface area   faster   fast slow particles
faster   faster   more often   collision   successful   slow   fast faster
low concentration   catalyst present   high concentration   large surface area

a) TEMPERATURE
Increasing the temperature will cause the particles to move _____ with more energy. They will therefore collide _____ _____ and with greater _____. These two things mean there are more successful collisions per second and therefore a _____ rate of reaction.

b) CONCENTRATION
Increasing the concentration of a reactant simply means there are more _____ which may collide and so react. More collisions means a _____ reaction.

c) SURFACE AREA
Using a powder instead of a lump means the _____ _____ is greater, which means a greater area of reactant is exposed and so available for a collision. More collisions means a _____ reaction.

d) CATALYSTS
Use of a suitable catalyst means that the particles may react even if they collide with only _____ energy. This means more _____ collisions are likely. Some catalysts work because one of the particles is fixed to a surface in a particular way. This makes the chance of a _____ more likely. More collisions means a _____ reaction.

Q3 Choose the sentence that **best describes** the collision theory:

- Particles collide at random and always react.
- Collisions between particles often result in a reaction.
- Reacting particles must collide with enough energy in order to react.
- Collisions between molecules are sometimes needed before a reaction occurs.

Module CD1 — Equations and Rates of Reaction

Experiments on Rates of Reaction

Q1 The reaction between sodium thiosulphate and hydrochloric acid produces a **yellow precipitate** of solid sulphur. This makes the solution **cloudy** and stops us seeing clearly through it. The **cross** below the flask in the diagram will slowly **disappear** as more precipitate is produced.

In an experiment to investigate rates of reaction, the time taken for the cross to disappear was measured.

50cm³ of sodium thiosulphate solution was used and 10cm³ of hydrochloric acid was added.

The experiment was repeated at different temperatures.

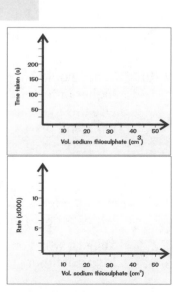

Temperature (°C)	20	30	40	50	60	70
Time taken (s)	163	87	43	23	11	5

a) Copy the graph on the right and use the results above to plot a line showing the relationship between temperature and time taken.

b) Use the graph to draw a simple conclusion about the effect of temperature on the time taken for the reaction to finish.

c) The rate of a reaction may be found by calculating 1/t. Copy the table above and add a row with the reaction rate at each temperature. Plot a graph of rate against temperature (you may have to use "Rate × 1000").

d) From the graph work out how temperature affects the **rate** of a chemical reaction.

e) Use your knowledge of the collision theory to **explain** your conclusion.

Q2 The graph shows an energy profile for a typical **exothermic** reaction.

a) Make a copy of the graph and mark on:

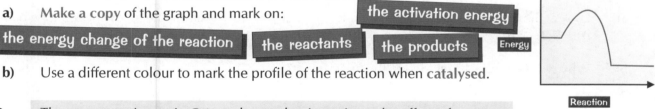

the activation energy

the energy change of the reaction   the reactants   the products   Energy

b) Use a different colour to mark the profile of the reaction when **catalysed**.

Q3 The same reaction as in **Q1** can be used to investigate the effect of **concentration** on the rate of a reaction. When changing the concentration, it is important to keep the total volume used exactly the same.

Volume of sodium thiosulphate (cm³)	50	40	30	20	10
Volume of water (cm³)	0				
Time taken (s)	80	101	137	162	191
Rate (1/t)					

a) **Complete** the table above, adding the volume of water and calculating the rate of the reaction (to four decimal places).

b) **Copy** the axes on the right. Then, using data from the table, show how the volume of sodium thiosulphate used affects the time taken and rate of the reaction.

c) Use these graphs to draw a **simple conclusion** about the effect of concentration on reaction rate.

d) **Explain** your conclusion in terms of particles and the collision theory.

Catalysts and Enzymes

Q1   Cheese goes mouldy after a while.

a)   What causes cheese and other foods to go off?

b)   Why does cheese stay fresh for longer if kept in a fridge?

c)   **Explain** why meat or vegetables in a freezer can stay fresh for months.

phew!

Q2   Suggest what part **enzymes** might play in the following pictures. Use the headings to help you.

(i) Laundry

(ii) Production of Cheese and Yoghurt

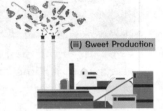
(iii) Sweet Production

Q3   The experiment below can be used to investigate enzyme activity.

Trypsin is an enzyme which acts as a catalyst to the breakdown of protein. Photographic film has a protein layer that holds the silver compounds in place (these appear black). Different films use different proteins. If the protein is destroyed this black layer falls off, leaving a clear plastic film.

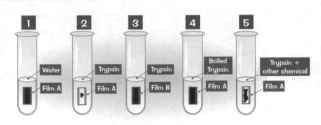

a)   Look at the test tubes carefully, then work out what you can say about the following test tube pairs:
i) 2 & 3   **ii)** 2 & 4   **iii)** 2 & 5

b)   Why was **test tube 1** included in the experiment?

Q4   An enzyme-catalysed reaction was carried out at **several pH** values. The graph opposite shows 'initial rate of reaction' against 'pH'.

a)   What do you estimate to be the **optimum pH** for the enzyme?

b)   What would happen to the enzyme if the pH was much **higher** or **lower** than the optimum?
Use this to explain why there is a very **low reaction rate** at pH 1 and pH 14.

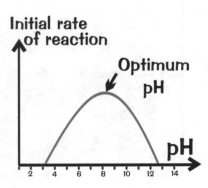

Q5   **Hydrogen peroxide** (H_2O_2) is toxic and is made in most living things. In the presence of a **catalase** enzyme it breaks down into harmless water and oxygen.

Suggest why you might expect the catalase enzyme in fish to have a **lower** optimum temperature than the catalase enzyme in humans.

Enzymes

Q1 The enzymes in **yeast** help to produce energy from sugar. They can do this by breaking down glucose into carbon dioxide and ethanol.

a) Write a **word equation** for this reaction.

b) Write a **balanced symbol** equation for this reaction.

The experiment was repeated at different temperatures and the volume of CO_2 recorded every 30 minutes. The results are shown in the table below:

Time (s)	Volume of CO_2 collected (cm^3) at temperature (°C)							
	20	25	30	35	40	45	50	55
0	0	0	0	0	0	0	0	0
30	0	0	1	3	3	1	1	0
60	0	0	2	6	6	2	2	0
90	0	1	3	9	9	3	3	0
120	1	1	5	13	13	4	3	0
150	1	2	7	18	18	6	4	0
180	2	3	10	25	25	8	5	0
210	3	5	14	35	35	10	6	0
240	4	7	18	45	45	12	7	0

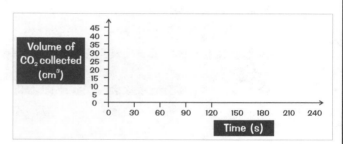

c) Use the results to **plot eight graphs** on the same axes. Set the axes out as on the right (for easy comparison, use different colours for each temperature).

d) From your graphs, which temperature(s) appear to be the **best working temperature(s)** for this enzyme?

e) **Explain** what happens to the enzyme at temperatures **above** these optimum temperatures.

f) The process of fermentation is very important. Name two major products that depend on fermentation.

g) What **unwanted** product would be formed if **air** was allowed in during fermentation?

Q2 Bacteria are used in the food industry as well as yeast.

a) Milk is the starting material for which **two** major foods?

b) Why is pasteurised milk normally used instead of fresh milk?

c) For one of the foods in your answer to **a)**, **describe** how it is made and the importance of the fermentation process.

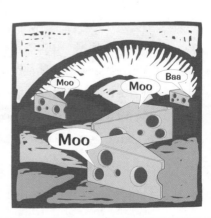

Enzyme — new fast acting formula includes bacteria...

Enzymes are made of protein — that's all they are. And their effect depends on their shape — so the enzymes that catalyse the browning of apples won't make you any yoghurt. Learn one or two examples, and don't forget how temperature and pH affect their efficiency — make sure you can draw graphs of these. And that's all there is to it. It's not like a foreign language or anything.

The Atmosphere

The graphs below give information about the Earth's atmosphere millions of years ago and today.

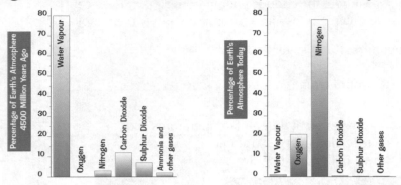

Q1   Could the early atmosphere **support life** as we know it? Explain your answer.

Q2   The **oxygen** and **carbon dioxide** levels in today's atmosphere are thankfully very different from how they once were. **Fill** in the blanks using the words in the box.

water vapour	evolved	oxygen	solidified	photosynthesis
degassing	volcanoes	carbon dioxide	ammonia	oceans

When the Earth's crust _____ many millions of years ago, _____ kept erupting and throwing out carbon dioxide, _____ _____ and _____ into the atmosphere. This is called _____. The water vapour cooled to form _____ which dissolved most of the _____ _____. Green plants _____ producing _____ and removing carbon dioxide by _____.

Q3   Study the above graph of **today's atmosphere**.

Approximately what **percentage** of the air is:
(i) oxygen
(ii) nitrogen
(iii) carbon dioxide?

Q4   About 3,000 million years ago simple organisms started to **photosynthesise**.

a)   Which gas did this **remove** from the early atmosphere?

b)   **Write** a word equation for the photosynthesis reaction.

c)   **Write** a balanced symbol equation for this reaction.

d)   Is photosynthesis an **endothermic** or an **exothermic** reaction?

Q5   Which organisms caused the **increase in oxygen** and the **decrease in carbon dioxide**?

Top Tips: All this boils down to <u>knowing</u> your atmosphere, and how its <u>composition</u> is affected by things like respiration, photosynthesis and burning. Learn the <u>rough percentages</u> for nitrogen, oxygen and carbon dioxide (for dry air — water vapour's pretty variable).

The Atmosphere

Q1 All living things respire. Write a **word equation** for respiration.

Q2 Gases like methane and ammonia were found in the Earth's early atmosphere. Look at the equations below and use them to explain the **changes** in the composition of the Earth's atmosphere.

> Ammonia + Oxygen → Nitrogen + Water
> $$4NH_{3\,(g)} + 3O_{2(g)} \rightarrow 2N_{2\,(g)} + 6H_2O_{\,(g)}$$
>
> Methane + Oxygen → Carbon dioxide + Water
> $$CH_{4\,(g)} + 2O_{2\,(g)} \rightarrow CO_{2\,(g)} + 2H_2O_{\,(l)}$$

Q3 Carbon that has been locked up for millions of years is returned to the atmosphere when fossil fuels are burnt. Write an **equation** for this reaction.

Q4 The diagram below shows the basic carbon cycle.

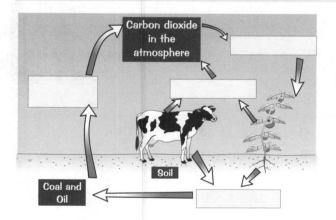

a) Copy the **diagram** and fill in the blanks using the following words:

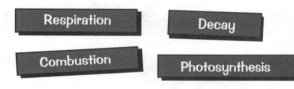

Respiration   Decay   Combustion   Photosynthesis

b) Use this diagram to explain why the levels of **oxygen** and **carbon dioxide** remain constant.

Q5 The sea and plants remove carbon dioxide from the atmosphere.

What will happen if processes that absorb the **additional** carbon dioxide released into the atmosphere from combustion of fossil fuels are **removed**?

Q6 Since humans have populated the world we have **destroyed** billions of acres of **forest** for farming and development — on average 16 million hectares are cut down every year.

Consider the graphs below and suggest a **possible effect** on the levels of **carbon dioxide** in the atmosphere if the Earth's forests continue to be destroyed.

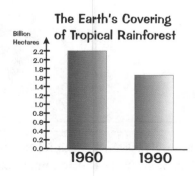

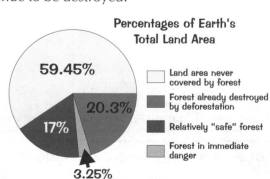

Crude Oil

Oil and natural gas have formed from the remains of plants and sea creatures. They are the result of the action of heat and pressure, in the absence of air, on plant and animal remains over millions of years.

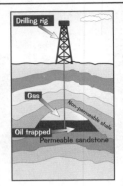
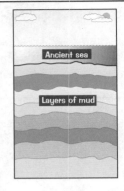

Oil and gas rise up through permeable rocks and become trapped under impermeable rocks. They are then extracted by drilling.

In the exploration for oil, geologists carry out test drilling to check for the rock formations that trap oil.

Most wells are 1000m - 5000m deep, but some can reach down 8km. Most of the oil is at high pressure, so is easily removed. Some deposits need water to be pumped down to force the oil out. The oil is transported in tankers or piped to a refinery where the crude mixture is separated.

Q1   Answer the following questions:

a) What is a **mixture**?

b) Crude oil is a **mixture** of what?

c) What is a **hydrocarbon**?

d) Give an **example** of a hydrocarbon.

e) **Why** is crude oil of little use without refining?

f) Oil is **non-renewable**. What does this **mean**?

g) Give three **advantages** and three **disadvantages** of burning oil products.

Q2   **Answer** these three questions:

a) **Heating** a compound supplies its molecules with what?

b) What do the molecules of a **liquid** do when heated?

c) What happens to the **molecules** when a hydrocarbon boils?

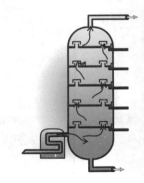

Q3   Oil is a finite resource.

a) What does **finite** mean?

b) What could **you** do to make oil last longer?

c) What could **all nations** do to make oil last longer?

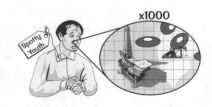

Top Tips: Oil is important — as a <u>fuel</u> and as a <u>resource</u> to make other useful things from. More importantly for you — it'll be in the Exam, so you need to know how oil <u>forms</u>, what it's <u>used for</u> and the <u>environmental problems</u> caused by burning oil.

Module CD2 — Energy in Chemistry

Fractional Distillation

Q1   What is **crude oil**?

Q2   What is a **fossil fuel**?

Q3   **What** are fractions A-E?

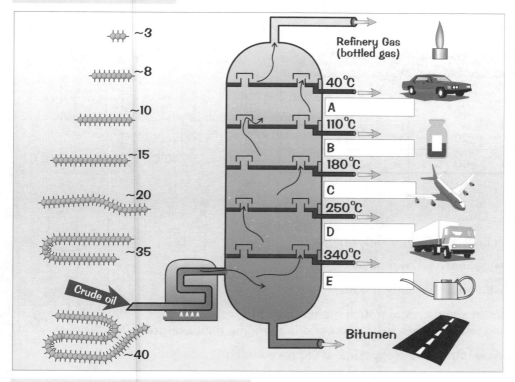

Q4   What do the following terms mean?

a)   Volatile   **b)**   Flammable   **c)**   Refining

d)   Boils off   **e)**   Fractions   **f)**   Distillation

g)   Viscous   **h)**   Refinery gas   **i)**   Carbon chain

Q5   Here are some questions about hydrocarbons, you lucky person...

a)   How does the **boiling point** of a hydrocarbon change as its carbon chain length increases? **Why** is this?

b)   The following paragraph describes how fractional distillation works. **Fill in** the blank spaces.

> Crude oil can be separated using _____ _____ because the covalent bonds between the _____ and _____ atoms are _____ than the _____ forces between the molecules. This means that fractional distillation does not change the properties of the individual fractions.

c)   Why is crude oil so **important**?

d)   How does the **flammability** of a hydrocarbon change as its carbon chain length increases?

e)   How does the **volatility** of a hydrocarbon change as its carbon chain length increases?

f)   Which would **flow** more easily — a hydrocarbon composed of short carbon chains or long carbon chains?

Hydrocarbons

If a liquid is quite <u>thick</u> and takes a long time to run down a slope, we say it's <u>viscous</u>.
We can measure how long it takes for a certain amount of liquid to run through a burette.
This will indicate how viscous the liquid is.

Lubricating oils in car engines prevent moving metal surfaces from touching. Viscous oils do this better than runny oils — but if they're too viscous they don't lubricate the moving parts properly.

Q1 The following experiment was set up to find which of two oils was the more viscous.
The time taken for the oil to run through the burette was noted at two different temperatures.

Burette	Temperature / °C	Time for 50cm³ to flow through / s
1	20	90
2	40	53
3	20	64
4	40	28

Use the table to answer these questions:

a) **Draw a bar chart** of the above information.

b) Which oil is the **more viscous** at 20°C?

c) Which oil is the **more viscous** at 40°C?

d) Temperatures in an engine are much higher than 40°C.
What will happen to the viscosity of these oils at **engine temperature**?

e) How could you **improve** the experiment to prove which
oil was the more viscous when used in an engine?

f) If you were designing an engine oil, would you use **short** chain
or **long** chain hydrocarbons?

g) What might happen to very viscous oil on a very **cold** morning?

Q2 **Complete** the following equations and **balance** them:

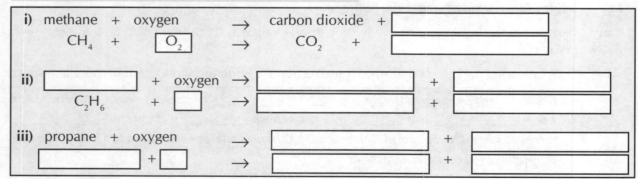

i) methane + oxygen → carbon dioxide + [ ]
CH_4 + [O_2] → CO_2 + [ ]

ii) [ ] + oxygen → [ ] + [ ]
C_2H_6 + [ ] → [ ] + [ ]

iii) propane + oxygen → [ ] + [ ]
[ ] + [ ] → [ ] + [ ]

What is the name of this type of reaction with oxygen?

Q3 Answer these questions about **incomplete** combustion.

a) Why is it **dangerous** to burn hydrocarbons in a limited oxygen supply?

b) Name two other **advantages** of complete combustion over incomplete combustion.

Alkanes

Alkanes are organic hydrocarbons that form a homologous series of hydrocarbons.
They only contain single covalent bonds and have the general formula C_nH_{2n+2}.

Q1   Copy the table and fill in the missing information:

Name	Formula	Melting Point(°C)	Boiling Point(°C)	Structural Formula
Methane	CH_4	-182	-164	H–C–H (with H above and below)
Ethane		-183	-89	H–C–C–H (with H's)
	C_3H_8	-190	-42	H–C–C–C–H (with H's)
Butane	C_4H_{10}	-138	0	H–C–C–C–C–H (with H's)
Pentane		-130	36	H–C–C–C–C–C–H (with H's)
Hexane	C_6H_{14}	-95	69	H–C–C–C–C–C–C–H (with H's)

Q2   Use the table to help you answer the following questions:

a)   Which **alkanes** are: **i)** solid   **ii)** liquid   **iii)** gas   at **room temperature** (25°C)?

b)   Each hydrocarbon molecule consists of atoms of **carbon** and **hydrogen**.
How many **atoms** of each (carbon and hydrogen) makes up a molecule of **pentane**?

c)   What is the **link** between the **boiling point** of alkanes and the number of **carbon** atoms they have?

d)   Why should a compound with **heavy** and **long** molecules have a different boiling point from a compound with **light** and **small** molecules?

Q3   Copy out the molecules of **propane, oxygen, carbon dioxide** and **water** opposite and use them to answer the following questions:

a)   Some bonds are broken when propane burns. On your diagrams, **ring two different** bonds that are broken.

b)   In a **different colour** (just for fun) ring two different bonds that are **made** when propane burns.

c)   Write a **balanced symbol** equation for this reaction.

H–C–C–C–H (propane structure with H's)

O=C=O

O=O

H–O–H

Butane

Top Tips: It is important to learn the <u>names</u> and <u>structural formulae</u>, and get an idea of the <u>physical properties</u> — just remember that melting point, boiling point and viscosity <u>increase</u> as the <u>number of carbons</u> increases, and volatility and flammability <u>decrease</u>.

Energy Transfer in Reactions

Q1 Fill in the blanks in the following passage (the words can be used more than once):

| energy | exothermic | endothermic | taken in |
| given out | negative | ΔH | break | made |

a) A reaction that gives out _____ is called an _____ reaction.
A reaction that takes in _____ is called an _____ reaction.

b) _____ reactions can feel hot as energy is_____ _____.
_____ reactions can feel cold as energy is _____ _____.

c) The energy change of a reaction is often given the symbol _____.
For _____ reactions the energy change is positive, ie. heat is needed.
A _____ energy change indicates an exothermic reaction, ie. heat is
released.

d) Virtually all chemical reactions involve _____ changes. Whether they
are _____ or _____ depends on the balance between the
_____ needed to _____ bonds in the reactant(s), and the
_____ released when bonds are _____ in the products.

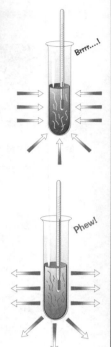

Brrrr....!

Phew!

Q2 Burning ethanol can be represented by the following equation:

$$C_2H_5OH + 3O_2 \rightarrow 2CO_2 + 3H_2O$$

You'll need this table of bond energies for questions 2 and 3

a) **What is** the energy needed to break all the reactant bonds?

b) **Work out** the energy released when all the product bonds are formed.

c) **Calculate** the overall energy change, ΔH. Is it **positive** or **negative**?

d) **State** whether the reaction is **exothermic** or **endothermic**.

Bond Energies (kJ/mol)

C—C	= 346
C—H	= 413
C=O	= 740
C—O	= 360
O—H	= 463
O=O	= 497

Q3 Consider the following reaction, and **calculate**:

$$CH_4 + 2O_2 \rightarrow CO_2 + 2H_2O$$

CO_2
+
$2H_2O$

CH_4
+
$2O_2$

a) The total energy needed to **break all** of the bonds of the reactants.

b) The total energy **released** in making the bonds of the products.

c) The total **energy change** (ie. the **net energy transfer**) for this reaction.

d) Is this an **exothermic** or **endothermic** reaction?

e) Give the **balanced symbol** equation for the **incomplete** combustion
of the same hydrocarbon.

Energy Transfer in Reactions

Q1   In the **Contact Process** for making sulphuric acid, sulphur dioxide is catalytically converted to sulphur trioxide:

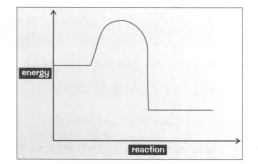

a)   **Mark** on the profile:

    i)   The reactants.

    ii)   The products.

    iii) ΔH (overall energy change).

    iv)   The activation energy.

b)   **Mark** on the diagram the profile you would expect for a reaction catalysed by vanadium (V) oxide.

c)   Is this an **exothermic** or **endothermic** reaction?

Q2   Here are some more **bond energies** (kJ/mol): $N\equiv N = 945$; $H-H = 435$; $N-H = 389$

a)   How much energy is needed to **break** the $N\equiv N$ bond?

b)   How much energy is needed to **break** the $H-H$ bond?

c)   How much energy is **released** when the $N-H$ bonds are formed?

d)   Write out the equation below using **structural** formulae for the molecules.

$$N_{2\,(g)} + 3H_{2\,(g)} \rightleftharpoons 2NH_{3\,(g)}$$

e)   **Calculate** the energy needed to break all the reactant bonds.

f)   Work out the **energy released** when the products are formed.

g)   Calculate the **overall energy change** (that's the **net energy transfer**) for the reaction. Is it an **exothermic** or **endothermic** reaction?

Q3   The apparatus opposite was used to calculate the energy produced by 1g of **ethanol**.

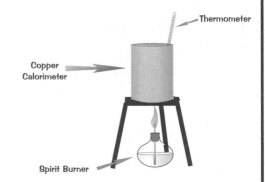

a)   Why is the calorimeter made of **copper**?

b)   The mass of ethanol burned was 1.6g. The calorimeter contained 200ml of water (specific heat capacity 4.18 J/g) and the temperature of this water was raised by 25.7°C. Calculate the **energy value** of ethanol in kJ/g.

c)   The actual energy value of ethanol is much **higher**. Give one reason why an experiment like this might not give very **accurate** results.

d)   Other than energy value, list **two other factors** which need to be considered when choosing a fossil fuel.

Energy transfer and heat — try to take it all in...

This sort of thing's difficult at first — but once it's <u>clicked</u>, you'll remember it. Don't forget that pulling things apart <u>takes energy</u> — so <u>breaking</u> bonds is <u>endothermic</u>, while <u>making</u> them is <u>exothermic</u>. Make sure you can calculate the total energy <u>change</u> of a reaction (ΔH) from <u>bond energies</u>.

Plate Tectonics

"Why haven't all the mountains on Earth worn away by now?" It's a good question.
A question like that could easily keep you awake for half the night. Anyway...

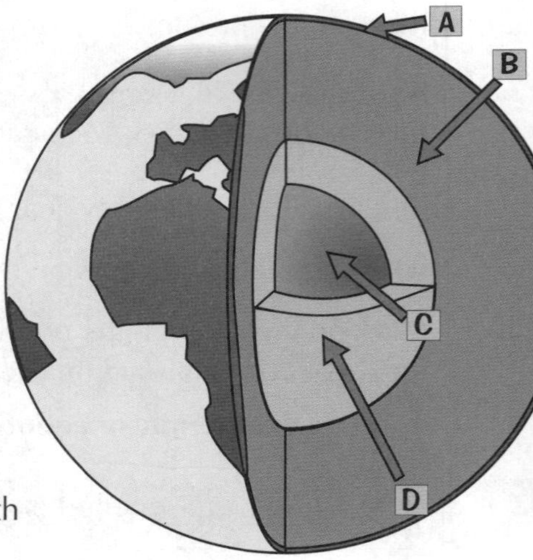

Q1   This cross-section of the Earth shows how it's made up.

a)   **What** do the labels A-D show?

b)   **Which** two elements make up both parts C and D?

c)   **Which two parts** are liquid?

d)   **How** was it possible for scientists to find this out?

e)   **Which parts of the Earth** could be responsible for
      the Earth's magnetic field?

f)   What is the general name for the cold outer part of the Earth
      that encompasses both the **mantle** and the **crust**?

Q2   **Complete** the following (short) paragraph by filling the gaps.

> The mantle is a layer of rock between the _____ and the _____. It has a _____
> density and a different composition from the rock in the _____.

Q3   How does the rock in the mantle that is nearer the
         crust differ from the rock that is nearer the **core**?

Q4   The **density** of the Earth's **crust** is much lower than the density of the
         whole Earth. What does this say about the inner parts of the Earth?

Q5   Roughly how fast are the plates moving?

A — 2 mm every ten years   **B** — 2 cm every day   **C** — 2 cm every year

Q6   Fill in the blanks in the passage about **mountain formation**, using some of the words in the box.

Mountain ranges are gradually .... by

weathering and .... but the

movement of the Earth's crust over a very long time forms

new ....

> rounded
>
> derision   worn down
>
> mountains   rivers
>
> erosion

Plate Tectonics

Q1   Explain briefly how **sedimentary** rocks are formed.

Q2   The following diagrams show cross-sections of different sea beds. For each
picture, describe the **processes** which could have caused the formation.

a)

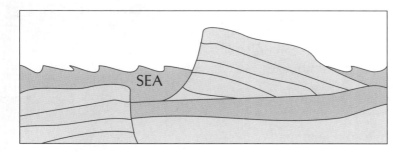

b)

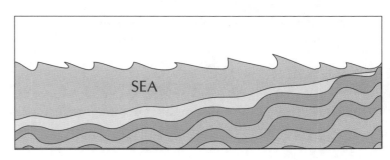

c)

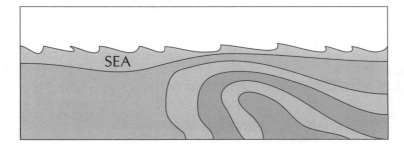

Q3   Fill in the blanks to explain how **metamorphic** rocks are formed.

Mountain belts were formed by movements of the Earth's ....

This process created .... rocks — which are evidence of the

high .... and pressures involved with the movements.

Q4   What is the name for rocks such as **basalt** and **granite**,
which are formed from the cooling of **magma**?

Plate Boundaries

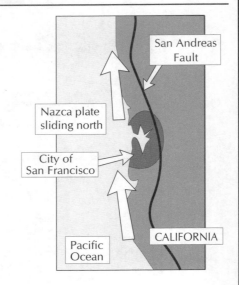

Q1   San Francisco is built on the boundary between two plates.
Along this famous San Andreas fault, one plate is sliding
past the other.

a)   Other than sliding past each other, name **two ways** that
plates can interact with each other.

b)   In 1906, there was a disastrous earthquake in San Francisco.
Describe briefly how an earthquake like this happens.

c)   **Describe one way** cities like San Francisco can protect
themselves from the devastation that earthquakes can cause.

Q2   The recent earthquake in Gujarat, India, measured 7.9 on the Richter Scale, and was devastating.
Similar strength earthquakes have happened in San Fransisco which haven't caused as much
damage. Give one reason why the Indian earthquake caused so much more devastation.

Q3   Here is a diagram of an oceanic plate and a continental plate being
pushed towards each other. **Label the diagram** using the words in the box.

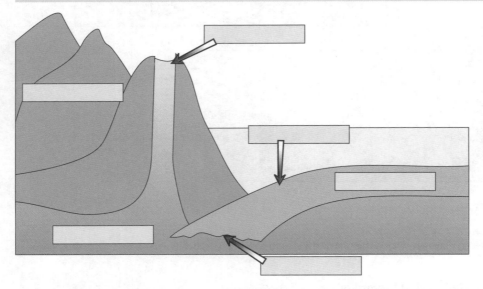

oceanic trench
folding
melting
oceanic plate
continental plate
volcano
magma

a)   As the plates move towards each other, the oceanic plate is pushed under the
continental plate. **What happens** to it as it is pushed down into the hot magma?

b)   What is a "**subduction zone**"?

c)   What happens to the continental plate as the oceanic plate is forced down under it?

d)   Why do **earthquakes** and **volcanoes** often happen in these areas?

e)   **Draw** some lava and ash flying out the top of the volcano. Ah go on...

f)   **Name one place** in the world where there is an oceanic trench formed in this way.

Plate Boundaries

Q1   When **oceanic plates** move apart, you get what's known as "sea floor spreading". Use this diagram to answer the questions below it.

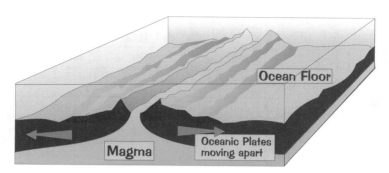

a)   As the plates move apart, **what happens** in the gap between them?

b)   Where plates move apart, you get symmetrical mountains on either side of the plate boundary.

What type of rock will these mountains be made of?

c)   **Give an example** of a place where sea floor spreading is occurring.

d)   The movement of the plates often causes undersea volcanoes.

What kind of **natural disaster** could be caused by an underwater volcano?

Q2   Fill in the gaps in this paragraph to explain how the **cooling of magma** in oceanic ridges has provided yet more evidence for continental drift.

The missing words aren't given on this one — so you'll really have to know your stuff.

As the .... move apart, liquid .... is pushed up to fill the gap.

As it solidifies, the .... particles contained in it align themselves with the Earth's

.... field, and set in position. This provides a record of the Earth's

magnetic field at the time when the .... cooled.

Scientists know that the Earth's magnetic field changes .... about every

500 000 years. This means that on either side of the ridge there are bands of alternate

.... polarity. These bands were discovered about 40 years ago, and

provided strong .... for continental drift.

Top Tips: I could have sworn this was Geography. Still, it's pretty interesting stuff — a nice break from all those formulae... but that doesn't mean the questions are easy. Make sure you've learnt the sciency facts <u>first</u> (there are a lot of them). <u>Then</u> learn an example of each feature. But get that science sorted first — it's the most important bit. Don't forget that — never ever...

The Reactivity Series of Metals

Q1   The Reactivity Series is a list of metals.

a)   What do you **understand** by the term "Reactivity Series"?

b)   Metals react with air, water and acids. What might you look for in such reactions to identify the **most reactive** metal?

c)   Put these metals in order of reactivity, starting with the most reactive:

| potassium | gold | aluminium | sodium | iron | copper | zinc |

d)   **Match** the following metals to the correct statement.

1) Sodium		**A)** Will not react with water or dilute acid.
2) Copper		**B)** Found alone not combined with anything.
3) Iron		**C)** Very reactive metal.
4) Gold		**D)** Corrodes in air fairly easily forming a substance called rust.

Q2   Carbon is between which elements in the Reactivity Series?

Q3   The diagram on the right shows the **blast furnace** used to convert iron ore to iron. Coke burns to form CO_2 which then reacts with more coke to make carbon monoxide. The carbon monoxide is a **reducing agent** and reacts with iron ore (Fe_2O_3) to make iron:

$$Fe_2O_3 + 3CO \rightarrow 2Fe + 3CO_2$$

a)   **Where** is carbon in the Reactivity Series relative to iron?

b)   **Explain** how the carbon monoxide reduces the iron ore.

c)   **Write** a word equation for the reaction given above.

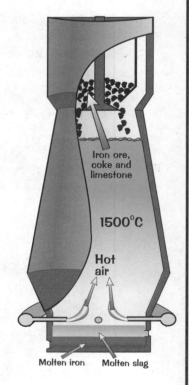

Iron ore, coke and limestone

1500°C

Hot air

Molten iron   Molten slag

Q4   Silver, gold and platinum are found **naturally** in the ground as elements and not as compounds.

Explain how this can happen.

Q5   Aluminium is much more **abundant** in the Earth's crust than iron, yet it is **much more expensive** to buy.

Explain why it is so expensive, in terms of its reactivity and the cost of extracting it from its ore.

Q6   Why do you think **gold** and **silver** can be worn next to the skin as jewellery, but other metals like sodium cannot?

REACTIVITY SERIES

Potassium
Magnesium
Iron
Gold
Platinum

Q7   Potassium has one electron in its outer shell, which is lost easily.

a)   Whereabouts in the **Reactivity Series** would you expect to find potassium?

b)   **Name** two elements that are above potassium in the Reactivity Series.

c)   Using the information given below, **place** metal X in the correct position in the Reactivity Series to the right.

METAL X — Very reactive, burns in air readily to form a layer of oxide. Reacts violently in water but does not ignite the hydrogen produced.

Metal Ores

Q1 Some metals form **ores**.

a) What is a metal **ore**?

b) Give an example of a metal ore.

c) In what form are very **unreactive** metals found in the ground?

d) **Give three examples** of unreactive metals.

e) In what form are **reactive metals** found in the ground?

Q2 The diagram below shows some of the processes involved in **extracting a metal** from its ore. **Label** each picture a) - f) with the correct expression from the following box:

Earth containing ore dug from the ground	Waste earth removed to concentrate ore

Pure metal	Carbon Reduction	Metal ore detected in ground	Electrolysis

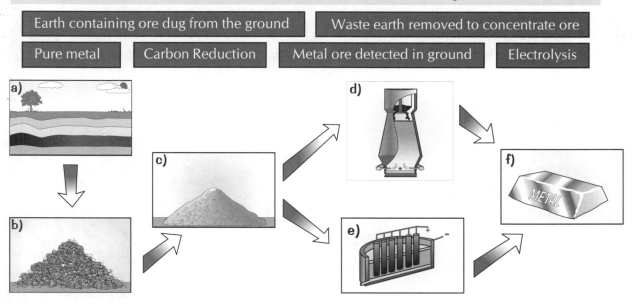

Q3 Which metal is extracted by which method?

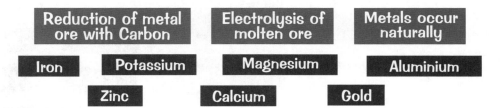

Q4 Coke is used to extract iron from its ore.

a) **Name** one other metal that could be extracted by reduction from its oxide by coke.

b) **Why** can't magnesium be extracted by reduction with coke?

Metal Ores

Q1 Choose the picture that best fits each of the substances described below. There may be more than one picture that fits each description.

a) A **pure** element.

b) A **pure** compound.

c) A **mixture** of elements.

d) A **mixture** of compounds.

e) An example of a pure compound made from just **two elements**.

f) An example of molecules made from **three elements**.

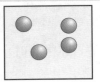 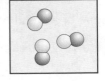

A   B   C

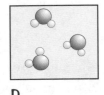 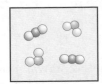 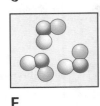

D   E   F

Q2 Mortar is a mixture of calcium hydroxide, sand and water. When the water dries out, the calcium hydroxide reacts with carbon dioxide to make calcium carbonate.

a) What **use** does it have?

b) What is a **mixture**?

Q3 Answer these questions about limestone's formation and uses.

a) What is the main substance in **limestone**?

b) What **type of rock** is it?

c) Why is limestone used as a **building material**?

d) What new material is formed when limestone is heated with **clay**?

e) The material in **d)** can be mixed with gravel. Give the **name** of this mixture and a **use** for it.

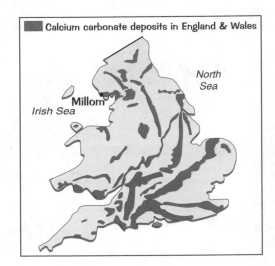

Q4 Many useful substances can be made from the rocks and minerals listed below. Match up the rocks and minerals with the materials on the right.

a) Clay

b) Sand

c) Bauxite

d) Rock Salt

e) Haematite

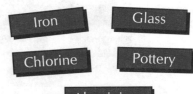

Iron   Glass

Chlorine   Pottery

Aluminium

Q5 Limestone is used in the blast furnace which is used to extract iron.

What **job** does it do in this extraction process?

Top Tips: Limestone is <u>mainly calcium carbonate</u>. Remember that limestone is also used to make even more useful products like <u>cement</u> and <u>glass</u>.

Module CD3 — Rocks and Metals

Extracting Iron: The Blast Furnace

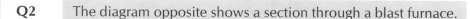

Q1   Iron can be extracted from its ore in a blast furnace.

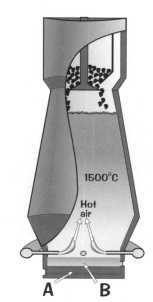

a)   **Explain why** iron can be extracted in this way,
      but sodium and aluminium have to be extracted by electrolysis.

b)   What is the **name** of the most common iron ore used?

c)   What element is the **iron bonded** to in this ore?

d)   What is the **formula** of this ore?

Q2   The diagram opposite shows a section through a blast furnace.

a)   Which **three solids** are put into the blast furnace?

b)   Why is **hot air** blasted into the furnace?

c)   Why does the blast furnace need to be heated above **1000°C**?

d)   What would you find at **A** and **B** in the diagram?

Q3   The first stage of the reduction process makes the gas carbon dioxide.

a)   **How** is carbon dioxide produced?

b)   **Write an equation** to show the reaction.

Q4   The next step — what does the **carbon dioxide** do in the blast furnace?

Q5   The final step involves changing the iron oxide into iron.

a)   **Write an equation** and balance it to show what happens.

b)   What has happened to the **iron oxide**?

c)   In what **state** is iron at the end of the reaction?

d)   How is it **removed** from the blast furnace?

Q6   In many chemical processes it is important to remove the impurities, to leave a pure product.

a)   What is the main **impurity** mixed with the ore?

b)   Calcium carbonate helps to remove this impurity, but first it needs to decompose.
      Complete the equation showing this decomposition: $CaCO_3 \rightarrow$ _____ + _____

c)   **Complete the equation** showing the formation of slag: $CaO + SiO_2 \rightarrow$ _____

d)   What can this **slag** be used for?

Top Tips: Metals are all pretty useful, but they tend to occur in the ground as ores.
Remember — the way you <u>extract</u> them depends on <u>how reactive</u> they are. You need to know the <u>blast</u>
<u>furnace</u> process for <u>iron</u> extraction — it comes up a lot in the Exam.

Extracting Aluminium

Extracting aluminium's a fiddly business for sure — but without it we'd all be climbing rope ladders...

Q1   Copy the diagram. Then fill in the missing **arrows** from the labels.

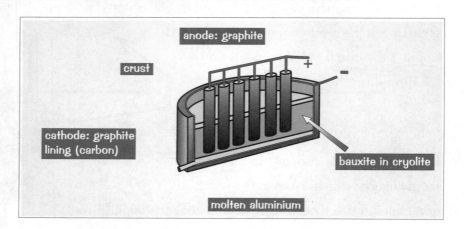

anode: graphite

crust

cathode: graphite
lining (carbon)

bauxite in cryolite

molten aluminium

Q2   **Complete** this paragraph using the following words:

reactive	aluminium	ore	difficult	aluminium
oxygen	bauxite	900		cryolite

Aluminium is much more _____ than carbon so is extracted from its

_____ using electrolysis. Aluminium is the most abundant metal in

the Earth's crust, and is joined up with other elements, rock and clays, which

make it _____ to extract. The main ore of aluminium is called

_____, which is impure aluminium oxide. It is purified, then dissolved

in molten _____ (another ore of aluminium) which lowers the melting

point from over 2000^{0}C to about _____ $^\circ$C. Electricity passes through

the melted ore separating the _____ from the oxygen. The overall

equation is: Aluminium oxide $\rightarrow$ _____ + _____

Q3   The extraction of aluminium is a complicated process.

a)   Why must the bauxite be **purified** before it undergoes electrolysis?

b)   Why is **cryolite** added?

c)   **Give two reasons** why adding cryolite is such a good idea.

d)   **Write out** the reactions that take place at the cathode and at the anode:

At the **cathode** (-ve): Al^{3+} + 3_____ $\rightarrow$ _____

At the **anode** (+ve): $2O^{2-}$ $\rightarrow$ _____ + 4_____

e)   At **which** electrode does **i)** reduction **ii)** oxidation   take place?

f)   **Why** do the carbon rods have to be replaced from time to time?

Extracting Aluminium

Q1 Aluminium has many uses. Some are shown in the diagram below.

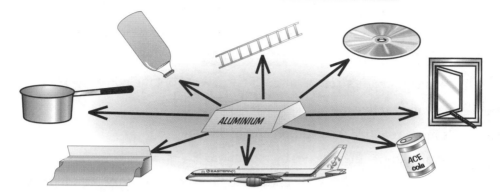

a) Label each of the above uses.

b) What properties of aluminium make it suitable for each application?

Q2 Have a coffee break and do this crossword about extracting aluminium from its ore.

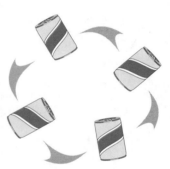

recycling - a damn sight easier than extracting.

Across
3. Aluminium ore is _____ to make aluminium oxide before electrolysis. (8)
4. During electrolysis, pure aluminium appears at the _____. (7)
5. Aluminium ore is called _____. (7)

Down
1. Aluminium oxide is dissolved in molten _____ to lower the cost of electrolysis. (8)
2. Aluminium oxide has a very high _____ point. (7)

Top Tips: It's tricky stuff — that's why aluminium extraction comes up in exams so often. You need to remember loads of scientific details, and also why they bother using cryolite in the first place... at the end of the day it all comes down to money.

Purifying Copper by Electrolysis

Q1   A lot of waste copper is now recycled.

a)   **What process** is used when recycling copper?

b)   **Give two reasons** why it is better to recycle copper than extract it from its ore.

Q2   Are the following statements true or false? If false, write out the correct version.

a)   Copper is a very **unreactive** metal.

b)   However, it's **more reactive** than carbon and hydrogen.

c)   **It's hard** to obtain copper from its ore by reduction.

d)   Copper obtained this way is **not pure enough** to be used in electrical conductors.

e)   Copper conducts **better** the purer it is.

f)   The copper produced from reduction is then electrolysed to produce **copper oxide**.

Q3   Copper can be purified by electrolysis.

a)   **Mark** (+) and (–) on the battery opposite.

b)   Copper metal in the impure anode becomes copper ions Cu^{2+}. Why do they travel towards the **cathode**?

c)   What do the copper ions **accept** when they reach the cathode?

d)   **Write** an equation to show this.

e)   **Write** an equation to show what happens at the anode.

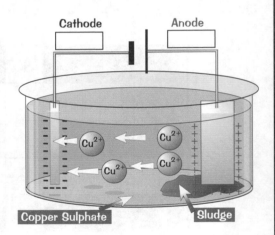

Q4   **Complete** the following paragraph using the words in the box.

You can use them once, more than once or not at all.

| purify | positive | splitting | electrolyte | sludge | electrolysis |
| electricity | electrons | copper | anode | copper metal |

_____ is the _____ of a compound by passing _____ through it.

It is used to _____ metals. _____ can be purified in this way. Copper

sulphate solution is the _____, which produces _____ ions and sulphate ions.

The impure copper is used as the _____ electrode, the _____.

This produces _____ ions which are attracted to the negative cathode. Here they

each gain two _____ to become _____ metal. A _____ from the

impure _____ forms underneath the _____.

Ions

Q1   Questions about ions here. Whoop-de-doo.

a)   What is an **ion**?

b)   Give **two** examples of ions made from single atoms.

c)   **Complete** this paragraph using the words provided:

-ve   protons   negatively   charged   neutral   positively   charged
Atoms are electrically _____ because they have equal numbers of _____ (+ve) and electrons (____). If electrons are taken away from an atom, then it becomes _____ _____ because it has less electrons than protons. If electrons are added to an atom, it becomes _____ _____ because it then has more electrons than protons.

Q2   Select from the list below. You may use each substance once, more than once or not at all.

SO_4^{2-} Mg^{2+} Kr   MgO CO_2 Cl^-

a)   An example of a **gas** consisting of **single atoms**.

b)   An example of an **anion** made from a single atom.

c)   An example of a **molecule**.

d)   An example of a **compound**.

e)   An example of an **ion**.

f)   An example of a **molecular ion** (compound ion).

Q3   Sodium hydroxide has many uses. It is obtained from rock salt industrially by electrolysis. What is **electrolysis**?

Q4   During electrolysis, ions gain or lose electrons at the electrodes. Electrically neutral atoms or molecules are released.

Balance the following half equation, which shows what happens at the cathode during the electrolysis of sodium chloride.

$$Cl^- \rightarrow Cl_2 + e^-$$

Q5   Answer these questions, covering some of the basics of ionic bonding:

a)   What is an **ionic bond**?

b)   If an atom gains an electron, **what charge** does it have?

c)   If an atom loses an electron, **what charge** does it have?

d)   What is a **cation** and what is an **anion**?

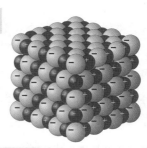

Ionic substances are tough but brittle — don't push them too far.

Waves

Q1 Copy the following sentences and **fill in the gaps**.

a) There are two different types of wave motion: _____ and _____.

b) The number of waves per second passing a fixed point is called the _____ and is measured in _____.

c) The time taken for two adjacent crests to pass a fixed point is called the _____ and is measured in _____.

d) The distance between a crest of the wave the centre line is the _____.

e) The highest point of a transverse wave is called a _____.

f) The lowest point of a transverse wave is called a _____.

g) The distance travelled each second by a wave is called its _____ and is measured in _____.

h) Waves will change their speed and wavelength when they go into different materials; this causes _____.

i) Waves will spread out when they pass through a small gap; this is called _____.

Q2 Describe the motion of the particles in an ocean wave.

Q3 Give a definition of **wavelength**. What unit is it measured in?

Q4 You can send a wave along a piece of string by shaking one end up and down (see diagram).

a) What do we call the up and down movement of the string?

b) How would you increase the frequency of this wave?

c) How would you increase its amplitude?

d) This wave is a transverse wave. Explain why a longitudinal wave of a similar frequency cannot be made to travel along the string.

Q5 What does a wave **transfer**?

Q6 You are floating in the sea, measuring waves (as you do). You time **5 seconds** between one crest passing and the next.

a) What is the **period** of this wave?

b) What is the **frequency** of this wave?

c) *By watching the waves move along a breakwater you estimate that the distance between 10 crests is about 30m.* Calculate the average **wavelength** of the waves.

d) **How far** have the waves travelled each time a crest passes you?

e) **How long** does it take the wave to pass you?

f) **How far** does the wave travel in one second?

g) What is the **speed** of the wave?

h) **Which way** do you move as the wave passes through you?

Waves

Q7   There are six equations below; some of which are incorrect.
Write down the correct versions, first in words, then using the usual symbols.

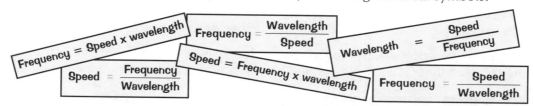

Q8   Copy and complete these sentences.

a)   For a wave travelling at constant speed, the frequency increases as the wavelength **increases / decreases**.

b)   For a wave travelling at constant speed, the frequency decreases as the wavelength **increases / decreases**.

c)   For a wave with a constant frequency, the wavelength decreases as the speed **increases / decreases**.

d)   For a wave with a constant frequency, the wavelength increases as the speed **increases / decreases**.

Q9   The diagram below shows a piece of string with a wave travelling along it.
There are beads attached to the string in positions A, B, C, D, E, F, G, H and I.

a)   Draw on the diagram where the stationary string would lie after the wave has died away.

b)   Which bead(s) are:

   i)   at the crests?

   ii)   at troughs?

   iii)   moving up?

   iv)   moving down?

   v)   changing direction?

   vi)   stationary?

   vii) moving with the greatest speed?

   viii) moving with the greatest acceleration?

c)   Calculate the amplitude, wavelength and frequency of the wave.

Q10   A certain radio stations broadcasts on a **wavelength** of 2.250km. If the
speed of radio waves is 3×10^8 m/s, calculate the **frequency** of the transmission.

Q11   A ruler was flicked on the side of a table and viewed under a rapidly flashing light
(stroboscope). The time between the flashes was increased until the tip of the ruler
appeared stationary. This happened when the light produced **48 pulses of light per second.**

a) Why did the ruler look like it was stationary under this light?

b) What is the period of oscillation of the ruler?

c) *The stroboscope flash rate is gradually decreased.*
The ruler appears to move again and then becomes stationary for a second time.
How many flashes per second is needed for this to happen? Explain your answer.

Sound Waves

Q1   What has to happen for a **sound wave** to be created?

Q2   In the objects below, what **vibrates** to start a sound?

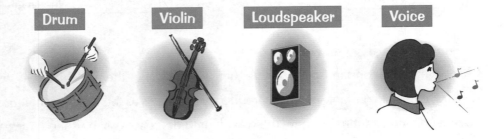

Drum   Violin   Loudspeaker   Voice

Q3   How does the vibration travel from the object to your ear?

Q4   **Sketch the diagram** below and complete the labelling.

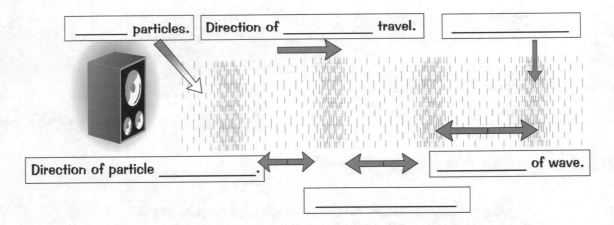

_____ particles.   Direction of _____ travel.

Direction of particle _____.

_____ of wave.

Q5   A spectator on a sports field is 200m from the start. She sees the starting gun fire and then hears the sound of the shot 0.6s later.

    a)   **Calculate the speed** of the sound.

    b)   What will be the **wavelength** of the sound if the frequency is 200Hz?

    c)   Another sound wave has a frequency of 2000Hz. How does its frequency compare to the wave in part **b)**? What will the ratio of their **wavelengths** be?

Light Waves

Q1   Like sound, light can be reflected off surfaces. Complete the gaps in the sentences below. The missing words aren't given, so you'll really need to know your stuff.

    a)   Some objects give out their own light. All other objects we see because they _____ light.

    b)   Some objects reflect light without sending it off in many different directions. This is called a _____ reflection and objects which do this look _____.

    c)   Most objects send the reflected light in many different directions, giving a _____ reflection. These objects look _____.

    d)   The law of reflection states that "the angle of _____ is _____ to the angle of _____."

Q2   What is the name for a beam of light used to represent a light path?

Q3   What is the name for the line drawn at right angles to a mirror surface?

Q4   The diagrams 1, 2 and 3 show rays arriving at a surface.

    Make a copy of each diagram. Complete the labels and draw the reflected rays.

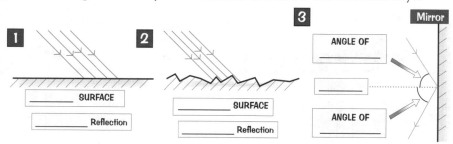

Q5   Study this plan view of two people sitting on a park bench.

    They can see some statues reflected in the window.

    Use the law of reflection to decide **which of the statues**, A, B, C and D, each person can see.

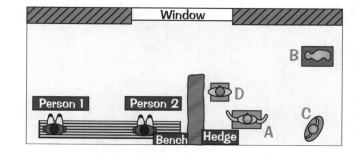

Q6   Study the rays in the two diagrams on the right.

    a)   In Diagram 1, a ray **enters** a glass block. Which ray (X, Y or Z) shows how it would continue?

    b)   In Diagram 2, a ray **leaves** the block. Which ray (A, B or C) shows its path correctly?

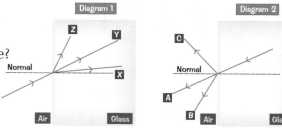

Q7   **Choose the right words** to make these sentences correct.

> When a ray of light enters a glass block it is bent [**towards** / **away from**] the normal.
> When a ray of light leaves the glass block it is bent [**towards** / **away from**] the normal.

Diffraction

Q1   Fill in the gaps in the following sentences about diffraction using the words provided.

spread out   gap   obstacle   diffraction   smaller   bigger

a)   Waves will _____ when they go through a _____ or past an _____.

b)   This effect is called _____.

c)   The _____ the gap the more diffraction there is.

d)   If the gap is much _____ than the wavelength, no significant diffraction takes place.

Q2   "Sound diffracts more than light."

Describe what this statement means and **explain why** sound behaves differently.

Q3   The following diagrams show plane waves approaching an obstacle.

a)
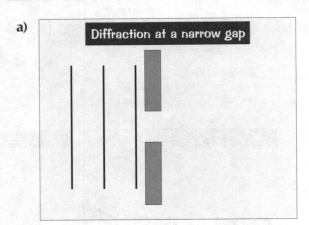

b)
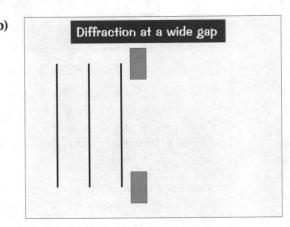

c)
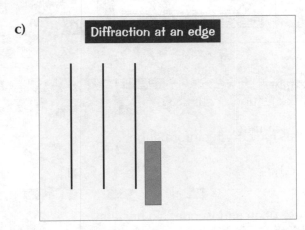

d)
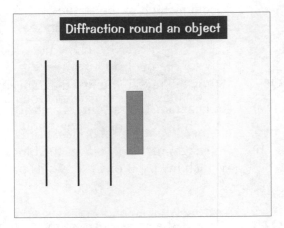

Copy the diagrams and draw the wavefronts after passing the obstacles.

Total Internal Reflection

Q1 The diagram shows two identical glass blocks with a ray entering at two different angles.

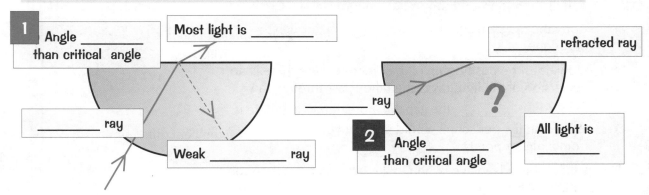

1 Angle _____ than critical angle

Most light is _____

_____ refracted ray

_____ ray

Weak _____ ray

_____ ray

2 Angle _____ than critical angle

? All light is _____

a) **Copy** Diagram 1 add in the normal and **complete** the labelling.

b) **Copy** Diagram 2. **Draw** the reflected ray inside the block and **complete** the labelling.

Q2 The diagram below shows a ray of light entering a glass prism at **right-angles** to a surface.

a) Why does the ray enter the prism without changing direction?

b) Copy the diagram opposite. Mark the normal, the angle of incidence and the angle of reflection, and label them.

c) What is the value of the angle of incidence at the inside surface?

d) What must be true about the angle of incidence and the angle of reflection?

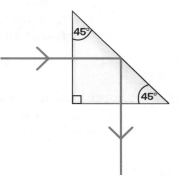

Q3 This is a question about optical fibres.

a) **Draw a diagram** of an optical fibre, showing:

> • the layers of the fibre
> • the light ray travelling along it (show 3 or 4 reflections)

Mark with arrows where total internal reflection occurs.

b) State the **advantages** of optical fibres over wires for carrying information.

Q4 **Describe** what an endoscope is, and give a use of an endoscope in a hospital.

Optical Instruments

Q1 The diagram opposite shows light entering a periscope.

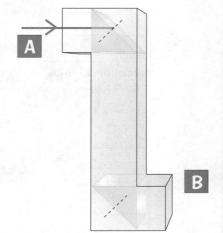

a) Copy the diagram and **draw the light path** through the periscope.

b) How does the positioning of the prisms ensure there is no dispersion of the light rays when they pass through the periscope?

c) Where on the periscope would you put your eye to view a scene from a higher point?

d) What is the advantage (when looking through the periscope) of lengthening the column A-B?

Q2 Give two uses for a periscope.

Explain why the periscope is needed in each case.

Q3 The diagram opposite shows a standard pair of binoculars.

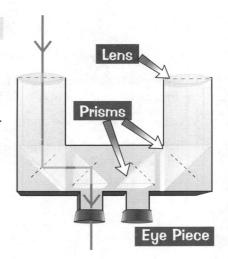

a) The lens and eyepiece are offset, so that prisms are needed to bend the light through the binoculars. **What is the reason** for this complicated arrangement?

b) **Complete** the light path for the other half of the binoculars.

c) Mirrors can be used instead of prisms. **Describe one advantage** of using highly reflective mirrors rather than prisms.

d) What property of the prism allows light to be 'bent' around corners?

Q4 The diagram below shows a light ray being reflected by a bicycle reflector.

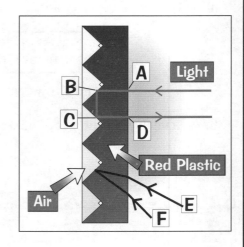

a) Explain how the incident ray is reflected back in the direction it came from.

b) What would you expect to happen to the light ray at 'E'? (Will it be reflected back the way it came or will it leave at a different angle?)

c) What will happen to the light ray 'F'?

Ultrasound

Q1 Copy and complete the following:

> "Sounds above 20 000Hz have too high a _____ to be heard by the human ear. Sounds above this frequency are called _____, and have a variety of uses."

Q2 Calculate the wavelengths of the following ultrasound frequencies (in air).

— Take the speed of sound in air to be 330m/s.

| **a)** 25kHz | **b)** 30kHz | **c)** 50kHz | **d)** 100kHz |

Q3 You should be able to describe several applications that humans have found for ultrasound.

Below is a table summarising six uses of ultrasound. The information is all mixed up.

Application	Category of use	Ultrasound used to	Basic principles
Removal of kidney stones	Industrial	Image the foetus	Use of energy in ultrasound to physically alter material
Quality control	Medical	Shatter stones allowing them to be passed out in urine	Use of energy in ultrasound to physically alter material
Removal of tartar	Military / Scientific	Break up tartar deposits on teeth	Use of energy in ultrasound to physically alter material
Sonar	Medical	Check for cracks in metal castings	Detection of reflected ultrasound to build image
Pre-natal screening	Industrial	Cleaning delicate mechanisms without dismantling them	Detection of reflected ultrasound to build image
Cleaning	Medical	Measure distances to objects or map the sea bed	Detection of reflected ultrasound to build image

Redraw the table with the information in the **correct places**.

Q4 Why is ultrasound...

a) better than X-rays for looking at a foetus?

b) better for cleaning delicate mechanisms than traditional methods?

c) better for treating kidney stones than open surgery?

d) the chosen method for checking for flaws in metal castings?

e) used to remove tartar?

WARNING: Applying ultrasound at the wrong moment can seriously damage the health of your baby.

Ultrasound — Liverpudlian for very good...

Most questions about ultrasound in the exam will ask you for details on its <u>practical applications</u>. Make sure you know them all properly. Also, remember the threshold of 20 000Hz — it's important.

Seismic Waves

Q1   The diagram shows the model we have developed
for the Earth using information from seismic waves.

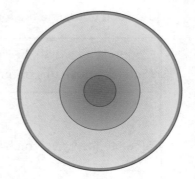

a)   **Copy** the diagram and label the different
layers that make up the Earth.

b)   The measurement of seismic waves can be
used to learn about the interior of the Earth.
Why is this a more convenient method than
drilling into the earth to take measurements?

Q2   Study the diagram of the Earth on the right. It shows
an earthquake sending four S–Waves into the Earth.

a)   Describe what an "**S–Wave**" is.

b)   What is the name for the region on the earth's
surface beyond X and Y?

c)   Why are there no S-waves detected beyond X and Y?

d)   Describe the **state** of the rocks in layer B.

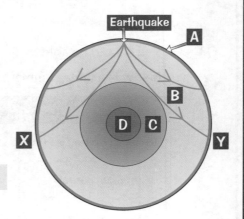

Q3   The paths of the **S–Waves** travelling through layer B are bent.

a)   What property of the rock in layer B changes
with depth to account for this observation?

b)   Now compare this effect with the refraction of light waves.
Give **two reasons** why we can say that the S–Waves in layer B are **refracted**.

Q4   Give **three** ways in which P–Waves are different from S–Waves.

Q5   The diagram below shows the paths for some **P–Waves** travelling through the Earth.

a)   Point D is at the boundary of which two layers?

b)   The direction of the waves at D and E changes
suddenly. Why does this happen?

c)   Detectors are placed on the Earth's surface
between points P and R. Describe where you
would **not** expect to detect any P–Waves.

d)   What property do P-waves have that allows
them to reach the parts that other waves can't?

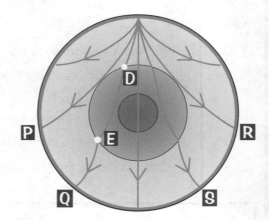

Q6   After an earthquake, would you expect to feel the
P–Wave first, or the S–Wave? Explain your answer.

The Electromagnetic Spectrum

Q1   Copy and complete the following paragraphs about electromagnetic waves.

a)   Electromagnetic (EM) waves form a continuous _____. For a given medium all EM waves travel with roughly the same _____. In a _____ this speed is about 3×10^8 m/s. There are _____ main types of EM wave. The correct order for these types of EM wave is (beginning with longest wavelength): _____ _____, _____, _____ _____, _____ _____, _____ _____, _____ and _____ _____.

b)   _____ waves have the lowest frequency and the _____ wavelength. _____ _____ have the highest frequency and the _____ wavelength. Our eyes are sensitive to EM waves from the _____ spectrum only.

Q2   Decide whether each of the statements a) to j) below is true or false. If false, write down what the highlighted words should be replaced with.

a)   **Microwaves** are used to communicate with satellites.

b)   **Microwaves** are the same thing as heat radiation.

c)   **Gamma rays** both cause and cure cancer.

d)   **Only visible light** will show diffraction.

e)   **Radio waves** can have wavelengths of many metres.

f)   **X-rays** are used to take pictures of bones because they are relatively safe.

g)   **Infrared** radiation causes skin cancer.

h)   **Microwaves** are absorbed by water.

i)   **Long wave radiowaves** are able to diffract long distances round the Earth.

j)   **Visible light** has a wavelength of about a ten thousandth of a millimetre.

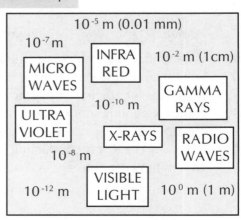

Q3   The diagram shows parts of the electromagnetic spectrum and wavelengths for the different radiations — but they're all mixed up.

a)   **Draw** your own diagram of a spectrum, but with the types of radiation and wavelengths in the correct order, from the shortest to the longest wavelength.

b)   What is the **speed** of an electromagnetic wave in a vacuum?

c)   Calculate the **frequency** for each type of wave.

d)   How many times longer is a typical visible light wave than an X-ray wave?

e)   How many times longer is a microwave than a typical visible light wave?

10^{-5} m (0.01 mm)

10^{-7} m

INFRA RED 10^{-2} m (1cm)

MICRO WAVES

GAMMA RAYS

10^{-10} m

ULTRA VIOLET

X-RAYS   RADIO WAVES

10^{-8} m

10^{-12} m

VISIBLE LIGHT 10^0 m (1 m)

The Electromagnetic Spectrum

Q1 This table is all mixed up. **Redraw** the table with the information in the **correct** places.

Type of Radiation	Effects on Living Tissue	Uses
Gamma	• probably none	• communication • broadcasting • radar
X-Ray	• heating of water in tissues can cause "burning"	• fluorescent tubes • tanning • security marking
UV	• kills living cells in high doses • lower doses can cause cells to become cancerous	• radiant heaters • grills • remote controls • thermal imaging
Visible	• kills living cells in high doses • lower doses can cause cells to become cancerous • kills cancerous cells	• kill bacteria in food • sterilise medical equipment • treat tumours
IR	• kills living cells in high doses • lower doses can cause cells to become cancerous • causes tanning	• imaging internal structures in the body • studying the atomic structure of materials
Microwave	• causes burning of tissues	• satellite communication • cooking
Radio	• activates sensitive cells in the retina	• seeing • optical fibre

Q2 Radiation absorption by biological tissues can have harmful consequences.

a) When radiation is absorbed, the energy it carries can be converted into **two** forms. Name them.

b) In general, is **low wavelength, high frequency** radiation more or less harmful than **high wavelength, low frequency** radiation?

c) Jessica Rarebit is sunning herself. Write down **two** ways in which she can protect against electromagnetic waves in the sunlight which are likely to cause **sunburn** or **skin cancer**.

d) Professor Lex Ray is conducting highly dodgy experiments with radioactive sources which are emitting gamma rays. What steps can he take to protect himself?

Radioactive Substances

Radioactivity has provided the plot for far too many really pointless movies.
But it <u>does have its uses</u>, and <u>examiners like asking about them</u> (the uses that is, not the movies).

Q1   The diagram below shows alpha, beta and gamma radiation being fired at a line of obstacles.

a)   **Copy** the diagram.
For each particle, draw a line to **show the path** it travels before it's absorbed.

b)   Give a reason why alpha particles only penetrate a **short distance** into a material.

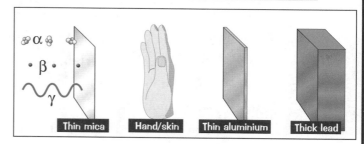

Q2   Radioactive iodine-131 is commonly used in medicine as a tracer.

a)   Explain what you understand by the word "tracer".

b)   Where will iodine-131 be concentrated if injected? Why is this?

c)   **What type of radiation** is emitted by iodine-131?

d)   Why would an alpha-emitting isotope be unsuitable for use in medicine as a tracer? **Give two reasons**.

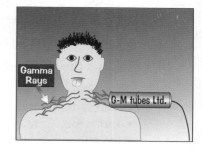

Q3   Radiation is used in the treatment of many cancers.

a)   **What type of radiation** is generally used?

b)   What does the radiation do?

c)   Why does the radiation need to be very well-targeted?

The medical physicists who are responsible for calculating the doses need to ensure that the dose of radiation isn't too low or too high.

d)   What could happen if the dose is **too low**?

e)   What about if the dose is **too high**?

It was a long time before anyone discovered what had happened to the children in the shed that day.

Q4   This question concerns the treatment of cancer using radiotherapy.

a)   High doses of gamma rays can be used to treat cancers. What effect do gamma rays have on living cells?

b)   **Explain** why a patient on a course of radiotherapy feels very ill.

c)   For the treatment to be a success, what two factors does the radiotherapist need to consider before starting the treatment?

Heat Transfer

Lots of people muddle up conduction, convection and radiation, which is pretty bad as they're totally different. Don't be a duffer — make sure you know the difference.

Q1 Below are a number of descriptions of heat transfer processes.
Are they concerned with **conduction**, **convection**, **radiation** or **all three**?

a) Heat flowing between two places when there is a **difference** in temperature.

b) Heat passing from **atom to atom** (most effective in solid materials).

c) Sets up movement **currents** in liquids and gases.

d) Is affected by **colour** and **shininess**.

e) Can occur through a **vacuum**.

f) Involves hot fluid **expanding** and **rising**.

Q2 This diagram shows a metal bar with a number of holes drilled into it. The holes are just big enough to fit thermometers in. Four thermometers are put into the holes, and initially read the same temperature. The bar is then heated at one end with a Bunsen burner.

a) Redraw the diagram showing the **levels** recorded by the thermometers after a few minutes.

b) Explain the levels you have drawn.

c) The same experiment was carried out using a bar of the same dimensions but made from a **poorer conductor**. Redraw the diagram to show this experiment's results.

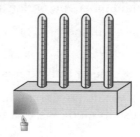

Q3 This paragraph is all about **heat conduction**. Use the words in the box to fill in the gaps. The words may be used once or not at all.

neighbouring collide carry reflect electrons pockets vibrate close good poor solids

Conduction is the main form of heat transfer in _____. This is because the particles

are relatively _____. Extra heat energy makes the particles _____ more.

They pass on the extra vibrational energy to _____ particles. Metals are

_____ conductors of heat energy because they contain many free _____

which can move through the solid and _____ the energy.

The electrons give up their energy when they _____ with other particles.

Q4 The diagram below shows water being heated in an **electric kettle**. The arrows represent **convection currents** in the water. Complete the following passage by circling the **correct words**.

Water next to the heating element is warmed and so [**expands** / **contracts**].
This means its density [**increases** / **decreases**] and so it [**rises** / **falls**].
Once away from the heating element, the water temperature [**increases** / **decreases**].
This results in it [**contracting** / **expanding**], which leads to a [**lower** / **higher**] density
and so it [**rises** / **falls**]. This cooler water is then heated by the element again and the
convection current continues.

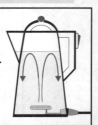

Heat Transfer

Q1 The diagram opposite shows an experiment involving **heat radiation**. Explain the following:

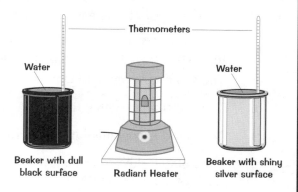

a) When the radiant heater is switched on, the **temperature** of the water in the dull, black beaker **rises faster** than the water in the shiny, silver beaker.

b) If the beakers are warmed to the same steady temperature and the heater is removed, then the dull, black beaker **cools faster** than the shiny, silver beaker.

Q2 Explain the following, using ideas of heat transfer:

a) **Frosty nights** in winter usually happen when there are **few clouds** in the sky.

b) In a hot water tank, the **heater** is generally at the **bottom**, and the **outlet** is usually at the **top**.

c) A layer of snow can **stop** young plants dying in the frost.

d) A shiny teapot keeps tea hot **longer** than a dull one.

e) Birds try to keep warm in winter by **ruffling** up their feathers.

f) Holding the legs of a transistor with pliers when it is being soldered can **prevent** heat damage to the transistor.

Q3 Below is a list of items that can help keep heat within a house.

Describe how each saves heat energy, and give the type of heat transfer that the insulation method reduces.

a) Curtains
b) Loft insulation
c) Cavity wall insulation
d) Hot water tank jacket
e) Double glazing
f) Draught-proofing
g) Thermostats

Q4 Write down three **insulating** substances and three **conducting** substances, then complete a table like this:

Name of Substance	Conductor or Insulator	Used for

Heat Transfer

Q1   Vacuum flasks have features which help them to insulate their contents.

Some features are listed below. For each of them, say **which method** of heat transfer they're reducing, and **how** they do this.

a)   The cap is covered in **plastic**.

b)   The cap is filled with **cork**.

c)   The liquid is contained in a **glass** bottle.

d)   The bottle is **double** walled, with a **vacuum** between the two walls of the glass bottle.

e)   The **outside of the inner** glass layer is silvered.

f)   The **inside of the outer** glass layer is silvered.

g)   The bottle is surrounded by **air** inside the plastic case.

h)   The bottle is supported away from the casing by insulating **foam**.

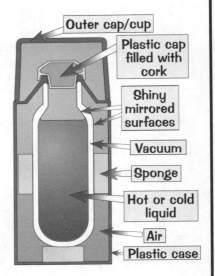

Q2   Liz and Damian are unhappy about their **heating bill**.

a)   Their annual bill is shown below. **Copy it** and then **fill in** the empty columns.

NAX POWER INDUSTRIES — giving you a real buzz...			
AVERAGE DAILY UNITS USED (kWh)	**TOTAL UNITS USED PER YEAR (kWh)**	**COST PER UNIT (PENCE PER kWh)**	**TOTAL COST (£)**
21.9		**6p**	

b)   Liz and Damian want to **reduce** the number of units that they use each day.
Give **two reasons** why Liz and Damian might want to reduce their daily energy consumption.

c)   Pete, a representative from Good Stuff Thermal Insulation, makes a call to the house one day. He suggests several ways in which his company's **products** could help reduce their energy usage.

Each of the suggestions is shown below. Calculate the **payback time** for each suggestion.

> Loft Insulation — costs £200, annual saving £50
> Double Glazing — costs £3000, annual saving £60
> Draught Proofing — costs £50, annual saving £50
> Cavity Wall Insulation — costs £600, annual saving £100
> Hot Water Tank Jacket — costs £10, annual saving 15

d)   Pete wants to save Liz and Damian as much **money** as he can on their bill, but they only have £2000 in savings.

i)   Which **methods** of energy saving can they afford?
ii)   They decide to buy everything except the double glazing. How much do they **spend**?
iii)   What will be the total **annual saving** on their heating bill?
iv)   What will be the total **payback time** for their whole purchase?

Domestic Electricity

Q1 Look at these two electricity bills from Rippov Electricity.

a) Complete the missing figures in these bills.

b) What is the scientific name for the term *"units"*?

c) If you were estimating the meter readings for a further quarter, what might they be?

Previous meter reading:	`4 7 0 4 1`	Previous meter reading: `2 6 9 3 5`
Present meter reading:	`4 7 5 2 5`	Present meter reading: `2 7 6 0 1`
Number of units used:	---------	Number of units used: ---------
Cost per unit (pence):	7.35	Cost per unit (pence): 7.35
Cost of electricity used:	---------	Cost of electricity used: ---------
Fixed quarterly charge:	£9.49	Fixed quarterly charge: £9.49
Total bill:	---------	Total bill: ---------
VAT on Total bill at 8.0%:	---------	VAT on Total bill at 8.0%: ---------
Final total:	£48.66	Final total: £63.12

d) If the bills were for the Summer quarter (May, June and July) what **difference** might you expect in a bill for the Winter quarter (November, December and January)? Explain your answer.

Q2 Here are some electrical appliances used at home:

microwave   toaster   lamp   vacuum cleaner   stereo

kettle   electric heater   hairdryer   TV   electric cooker

Which four appliances are the most expensive to run (for a given length of time)?
What do they have in common?

Q3 **Fill in** the gaps below.

a) These are units of energy:

_ _ _ _ _ _ _ _ _ _ _

"Units"
kWh J kJ
kW W

b) These are units of power:

_ _ _ _ _ _ _

c) "deci" means:

_ _ _ _ _ _ _ _ _

100 1000
10 10,000 1⁄10
100,000

d) "kilo" means:

_ _ _ _ _ _ _ _ _

Q4 **Copy and complete** the table opposite to work out how many joules a hairdryer uses in one hour.

Power (kilowatts):	1 kW
Time switched on (in hours):	1 h
Power in watts:	-------------
Time switched on (seconds):	-------------
Energy used (in kilowatt hours):	-------------
Energy used (in joules):	-------------

Q5 This paragraph is about the **advantages** and **disadvantages** of using electricity in the home. Use the words in the box to fill in the gaps. The words may be used once or not at all.

appliances storage countryside pollution easy power cut cables disadvantages toasters shock storage

The main advantage of having electricity as an energy supply is that it's really _____ to use. It can be used to operate lots of different _____ around the home, such as _____. Once it gets to your house, electricity causes no _____ whatsoever. There are no _____ problems either, since it comes straight down the power lines and directly to your home. Unfortunately, there are some _____ too. If you're not careful then electricity can give you a nasty _____, and any problems at the power station may well result in an annoying _____. Also, the only way to get electricity to the house is through _____. This can be a big problem, especially if you live in the _____.

Domestic Electricity

Q1 **Copy and complete** the following summary using these words:

> joules energy twice energy voltage previous take

To find the number of units used on an electricity bill, _____ the _____ meter reading from the present meter reading. You pay for the _____ you have used, not the _____ or current supplied. If a label on an appliance says "1kW" it means it will use _____ at the rate of 1000 _____ per second. A "2kW" appliance uses energy _____ as quickly as a "1kW" appliance.

Q2 Work out the energy consumed by the following (in kWh):

    a)   100W lamp for 10 hours   **b)**   10W mains radio for 5 hours

    c)   500W microwave for 1/2 hour   **d)**   100W electric blanket for 1 hour

Q3 **Find the cost** (at 10p/unit) of using:

    a)   An electric drill, power 300W for 2 hours.

    b)   A 20W hairstyling brush for 1/2 hour.

    c)   Two 100W electric lights on for 9 hours a day for a week.

    d)   A 900W toaster for 15 minutes every day for a month (30 days — it's September!).

    e)   Four 60W electric lights on 12 hours a day for an old-fashioned working week (5 days).

Q4 Work out which of the two appliances consumes the most energy.

    a)   A 2kW heater for 4 hours   ***or***   a 3kW fire for 3 hours.

    b)   A 900W toaster for 15 minutes   ***or***   a 800W vacuum cleaner for 20 minutes.

    c)   A 300W drill for $^1/_2$ hour   ***or***   a 100W light bulb for 1 $^1/_2$ hours.

    d)   A 1kW iron for 1 hour   ***or***   a 2kW kettle for 20 minutes.

    e)   A 2.1kW immersion heater for 1 hour   ***or***   a 1.5kW fire for $^1/_2$ hour.

Q5 The following table summarises the initial and running costs of filament lamps and CFL (compact fluorescent) lamps.

Type of Lamp	Lifetime of lamp (h)	Power (kW)	Cost of 1kWh of electricity (£)	Cost of electricity for lamp's lifetime (£)	Cost of 1 lamp (£)	Total running and purchase cost for 12000 hr. (£)
CFL	12000	0.02	0.1		10.00	
Filament	1000	0.1	0.1		0.50	

    a)   **Copy and complete** the table.

    b)   Give **two benefits** of CFL lamps over filament lamps.
             (A 20W CFL lamp gives the same amount of light as a 100W filament lamp.)

Top Tips: The <u>units</u> that electricity meters measure are <u>kilowatt-hours</u> (kWh). That means the amount of electrical <u>energy</u> used by a <u>1kW</u> appliance left on for <u>1 hour</u>. Don't be confused by the name, it isn't a measurement of power, it's a measurement of energy.

Domestic Electricity

Q1 Complete the following sentences about **Economy 7**, using the words given below:

night   expensive   power stations   storage heaters   day

cheaply   dishwashers   immersion heaters

a) Economy 7 is a pricing scheme where electricity supplied during the _____ is especially cheap.

b) During the night, _____ are heated up. The heat can then be released slowly over the course of the _____.

c) Some household appliances, such as _____, can be left running during the night.

d) This means that they can be operated more _____ under the Economy 7 scheme.

e) Economy 7 electricity is slightly more _____ than normal electricity during the day.

f) The scheme is cost-effective for the electricity company. This is because _____ can't just be turned off at night.

Q2 Below is a portion of an **electricity bill**. It shows the electricity used by a household over a 90-day period. There is also a table showing the **tariffs** for an Economy 7 pricing scheme.

Pricing Scheme	Economy 7
Total no. of days used	90
No. of units used at low rate	350
No. of units used at normal rate	900

14p	Daily Fixed Charge
3p	Per unit supplied at night (low rate)
6p	Per unit supplied during the day (normal rate)

What is the **total cost** of the electricity used during this period?

Q3 State the electrical **hazard** in each diagram below, and say what you would do to make each one safe.

a)   b)   c)   d)

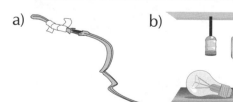

Q4 Write down as many other electrical hazards in the home as you can think of.

You should be able to write down at least **six**.

**Safety Features**

Q1   Everyone should learn how to wire a plug.

Label **A - C** on the plug on the right with:
green and yellow, blue, brown, live, earth, neutral.

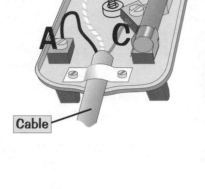

Q2   **Which parts** of the plug are made out of the following materials, and why?

a)   **brass** or **copper**

b)   plastic

Q3   Write a **check list** of five things you would check to make sure a newly wired plug is completely safe.

Q4   Radios, TVs and lamps do not usually have an earth wire.

a)   What is the **function** of the earth wire?

b)   Why are appliances like TVs safe to use **without** an earth wire?

Q5   **Copy** the diagram below. Now use arrows to join the two wires to their appropriate **function**:

Live

Neutral

Is always at **0V**. It is the wire which **completes** the circuit.

Carries a **high voltage**

Q6   Complete the following paragraph:

Use these words: _safety, alternating, neutral, live, 230, earth, voltage_

The _____ of a live wire is an _____ voltage of _____V.

Electricity normally flows along the _____ and _____ wires only.

The _____ wire is just for _____.

Q7   Answer the following questions on fuses.

a)   Why do we use fuses?

b)   What is **inside** a fuse?

c)   **Explain** what happens when a fault causes a 6A current in an appliance fitted with a 3A fuse.

d)   Why should you not use a 1A fuse in a hairdryer plug?

e)   **Explain** what would happen if the live wire in a toaster touched the metal case.
Say how the earth wire and the fuse work together to make the appliance safe.

Safety Features

Q1 The table below shows seven appliances and the current in them.

For each appliance, decide if it needs a 3A, 5A or a 13A fuse. (The first one is done for you.)

Appliance	Current taken (A)	Fuse value (A)
Food Mixer	2	3
Cassette Player	3	
Hairdryer	4	
Electric Heater	12	
Toaster	4	
Kettle	9	
Vacuum Cleaner	3.5	

Q2 This diagram shows a kettle circuit that has been drawn incorrectly.

a) Find the **four** mistakes.

b) **Redraw** the circuit correctly.

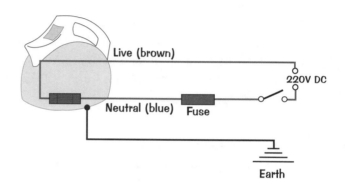

Live (brown)

220V DC

Neutral (blue)   Fuse

Earth

Q3 **Fill in the gaps** in the box below, using the given words.

cover   blown   expert   wired   fuse   earth   replace

Appliance: Must be correctly _____ to a plug fitted with the correct _____ and with an _____ wire connected to any touchable metal part.

Blown Fuses: You must find out why a fuse has _____. If this is not obvious, consult an _____. Do not _____ the fuse with one of a higher rating.

Fire Risk: Never _____ an appliance, particularly with something that can burn.

Q4 Study the diagram below of a domestic electricity supply. What happens to the **lights** in the kitchen, lounge and dining room and the **hairdryer** if:

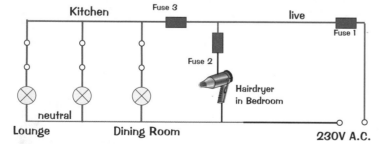

Kitchen   Fuse 3   live

Fuse 1

Fuse 2

Hairdryer
in Bedroom

neutral

Lounge   Dining Room   230V A.C.

a) fuse 1 blows?

b) fuse 2 blows?

c) fuse 3 blows?

Fuses — they die so that your kettle may live...

Just because you always get a leaflet with your toaster saying what fuse it needs, it doesn't mean you'll never have to work it out for yourself. You might lose the leaflet. It might be a question on The Weakest Link. It might even be in your GCSE Science Exam too. You never know...

Velocity and Acceleration

This section is based on the thinkings of Sir Isaac Newton. His ideas now allow us to work out loads of things such as how far we have gone and how fast we got there – great.

Q1   **Calculate the speed** of the items below in m/s:

a)   An athlete who runs 100m (metres) in 10s (seconds).

b)   A racing car zooming 240m in 12s.

c)   A student, walking 360m in 240s.

d)   A tortoise with a twisted ankle, shuffling 10m in 100s.

Q2   How long?

a)   My flashy neighbour reckons his new racing bike can reach 18 m/s. He finished 10 laps of a 120m track in 70s. **Work out** his speed. **Could** he be telling porky pies?

b)   A sprinter crosses the 100m race finish line. His speed throughout the race was 10 m/s, so **how long** did it take him?

c)   The greyhound racetrack is 750m long. If Droopy's speed is 25 m/s, **what** is his time?

Q3   How far?

a)   **How far** around the track would a racing car get, going at 90 m/s for 30s?

b)   Concorde can travel at 650 m/s. **How far** can it go in 25s, travelling at this speed?

c)   Find **how far** a cheetah could get if its speed is 30 m/s (70 mph) and it runs for 500s.

d)   **How far** would a roadrunner go travelling at a speed of 25 m/s (56 mph) in 700s?

Q4   **Complete the sentences** using words from the list below.

fast   direction   how   direction

> Speed is _____ _____ you're going with no regard to _____ .
> Velocity, however, must also have the _____ specified.

Q5   A car travels 600m in 30s.

a)   Find its average **speed**.

b)   The car's average speed is usually different from its speed at any particular instant in time. **Explain** the reason for this.

c)   **How far** would the car travel at the same speed in 1500s?

Q6   **Find** the speed (in m/s) of:

a)   A train going 1200km in 8 hours.

b)   A walker who travels 12km in 2½ hours.

Q7   **How** far does:

a)   A cyclist travel in 3 hours at an average speed of 12 km/h?

b)   A ship travel in 5 hours at an average speed of 25 km/h?

Velocity and Acceleration

Q1   **How long** does it take:

a)   A car to cover 560km at an average speed of 70 km/h? (in hours)?

b)   Light to travel from the Sun to the Earth (150,000,000 km) at a
speed of 300,000 km/s? (Answer in minutes and seconds.)

Q2   Find the velocity of a walker travelling a distance of 1000m east in 500s.

Q3   Find the velocity of a bird flying 450m south-east in 5s.

Q4   A walker starts in Barchester at 10am. She walks 5km north-nast to Histon, getting there
at 11am. She takes a half-hour break, then walks back to Barchester in 50 minutes.

a)   What is her **velocity** (in m/s) when walking to Histon?

b)   What is her **velocity** when walking back to Barchester?

c)   What is her **average speed** for the whole trip?

Q5   Here's a really useful equation in a fantastic grey box:

a)   From the equation, state what **a**, **v**, **u** and **t** stand for.

b)   State the usual **units** of **a**, **v**, **u** and **t**.

c)   **Explain** how acceleration is different from speed and velocity.

$$a = \frac{v - u}{t}$$

Q6   **Complete these sentences** using words from the list below. Use each word once only.

acceleration,   second,   3 m/s,   second,   acceleration,   4 m/s,   velocity,   velocity

a)   A motorbike has a steady _____ of 3 m/s². This means that
every _____ its _____ changes by _____.

b)   A car has a steady _____ of 4 m/s². This means that every
_____ its _____ changes by _____.

Q7   PC Bacon is cruising along in his car at 15 m/s.

a)   He keeps on going for an hour. **How far** does he go, in kilometres?

b)   A car shoots past at 80 mph. One mile is about 1.6 kilometres.
How fast is the car going in kilometres per hour, and in metres per second?

c)   PC Bacon gives chase, and accelerates steadily at 1 m/s² up to 40 m/s. **How
long** does this take?

d)   After travelling along for 3 minutes at 40m/s, he catches up with the speeding car. **How far** has
he travelled since reaching 40 m/s?

e)   The speeding car is now travelling at 28 m/s. PC Bacon flags it down, and it pulls over into a lay-
by. The car takes 15s to halt, **what** is its deceleration?

Was I speeding, officer?...   Speed and velocity — they're not the same.
They both say how fast a thing is going, but velocity also gives the direction, e.g. 30 m/s North.
Remember Speed = Distance ÷ Time — writing them in a formula triangle makes everything a lot easier.

D–T and V–T Graphs

Q1 This question is about a car whose motion is described by a velocity-time graph.

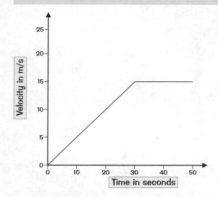

a) **How far** does the car travel in the first 30 seconds?

b) **Describe** the motion of the car in the next 20 seconds.

c) **Copy** the graph with the time axis extended to 100 seconds. Then **complete** the graph using the following information:

(1) Between the times of 50 and 60 seconds, the car undergoes a steady acceleration to 20 m/s.

(2) For the next 20 seconds the car's speed is steady at 20 m/s.

(3) During the next 20 seconds, the car slows to a stop at a steady rate.

d) **Calculate** the acceleration occurring in **c) (1)**.

e) **Calculate** the deceleration occurring in **c) (3)**.

f) **Work out** the distance travelled during the last 40 seconds of this short trip.

Q2 This question is about Barry riding his new bike.

a) **How far** does Barry travel during the first 20 seconds of his journey?

b) What is Barry's deceleration during the **second** 20 seconds of his journey?

c) **How far** does Barry travel during the period of deceleration described in **(b)**?

d) What happens over the **next 20 seconds** of the journey?

e) **How far** has Barry travelled in total over the whole 60 seconds?

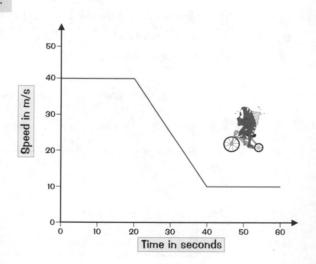

Q3 **Draw** a distance-time graph using these measurements taken during a bike journey.

Distance (m)	Time (s)
0	0
20	5
40	10
60	15
80	20
100	25
100	30
50	35
0	40

a) **Describe** the motion of the bike for the whole journey (write on the graph).

b) **Calculate** the speed of the bike between the times of 20 and 25 seconds.

c) **For how long** is the bike stationary?

d) **Calculate** the speed of the bike between the times of 30 and 40 seconds.

D–T and V–T Graphs

Q1 A car passes a crossing. Its distance from the crossing is measured every second.

Distance (m)	Time (s)
0	0
2	1
9	2
18	3
27	4
36	5
45	6
54	7
54	8

a) **Plot a graph** of distance in metres (vertical axis) against time in seconds (horizontal axis).

b) **Mark** on the graph where the car (i) is accelerating, (ii) is travelling at a steady speed, (iii) is stopped.

c) What is the **average speed** of the car in the first 7 seconds?

d) **What distance** has the car travelled after 5.5 seconds?

e) **How long** did the car take to travel 23 metres?

Q2 **Complete** the table by stating the significance of features sometimes observed on Distance-Time and Velocity-Time graphs.

Feature on Graph	Distance/Time	Velocity/Time
Gradient equals		
Flat sections show		
Curves show		
Downhill section shows		
Area under the curve shows	NOT APPLICABLE	

Q3 This question is about the motion of a motorbike described by a distance-time graph.

a) **What** is the **maximum** speed of the motor bike?

b) **What distance** does the motor bike travel in the first 20 seconds?

c) **Calculate** the motor bike's speed between 20 and 40 seconds.

d) **Describe carefully** how the motor bike moves during the 60 seconds (use words like accelerates, decelerates, steady speed).

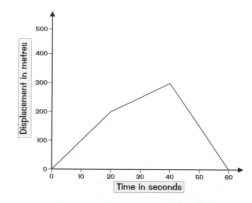

Q4 **Draw** a velocity-time graph using these measurements taken during a car journey.

a) **Describe** the motion of the car (**write on the graph**).

b) **Calculate** the acceleration of the car in the first 12 seconds.

c) If the car had a mass of 1000 kilograms, **what force** was needed to produce the acceleration in (b)?

d) **Calculate** the deceleration of the car in the last 4 seconds.

Velocity (m/s)	Time (s)
0	0
4	2
8	4
12	6
16	8
20	10
24	12
24	14
24	16
12	18
0	20

84

Force Diagrams

Q1   Use the list on the right to identify forces **a)** to **f)**.

a) Acts straight downwards.	TENSION
b) Slows things down.	GRAVITY or WEIGHT
c) In a rope or cable.	LIFT
d) Due to an aeroplane wing.	THRUST or PUSH or PULL
e) Speeds something up.	REACTION FORCE
f) Acts straight upwards on a horizontal plane.	DRAG or AIR RESISTANCE or FRICTION

Q2   This question concerns a stationary object — a mug of tea — Mmm, nice.

a) **Copy** the diagram and **draw in** the two vertical forces. **Label them**.
b) **Explain** how you know that this pair of forces is equal.
c) **What** would happen if there was only one **vertical** force?

Q4   A car is moving forward with a **steady** horizontal velocity.

a) **Copy** the diagram and **draw in** the two vertical forces. **Label them**.
b) **Draw** in the **two** horizontal forces. Is one force bigger than the other?

Q5   **Complete** the following sentences with the words below:

unbalanced   faster   greater   greater   thrust   upwards
downwards   weight   reaction   drag   drag   force   smaller

Acceleration means "getting _____". You only get acceleration with an overall resultant (_____) force. The _____ the unbalanced _____ the _____ the acceleration. The _____ the unbalanced force, the smaller the acceleration. A car which is accelerating forward has a larger _____ than _____ force, but the vertical forces (_____ and _____) are the same. A skydiver accelerating _____ has a weight force downwards, but less _____ _____.

Q6   Use **Newton's Laws** to answer these questions.

a)   If an object is stationary and has no forces acting on it, **what happens**?
b)   If an object is moving at a steady speed over a rough surface but has no forces propelling it along, **what happens**?
c)   What does an object need in order to continue travelling at a steady speed across a rough surface. **Why**?

PD3 — Forces and Motion

Force, Mass and Acceleration

Q1　**Find** the acceleration of:

a)　A cat, pouncing from 0 m/s to 5 m/s in 4s.

b)　A car, speeding from 10 m/s to 30 m/s in 5s.

c)　A runner, going from 3 m/s to 8 m/s in 3s.

Q2　Newton's First Law of Motion states that "**balanced forces**" means no change in "**velocity**".

a)　**Explain clearly** "balanced forces" and "velocity".

b)　**Draw a diagram** of something (a car, bus, stick man) moving at a constant velocity. **Draw in** the horizontal forces.

c)　**Describe** what is meant by the term "resultant" force.

d)　For your diagram in **b) what** is the resultant force?

Q3　**F = ma** (Force = mass x acceleration)

a)　**What** are the units of F, m and a?

b)　**Rearrange** the equation as "a = ".

c)　**Rearrange** the equation as "m = ".

Q4　**Find** the acceleration of these objects:

a)　Resultant Force 100N, mass 10kg.

b)　Resultant Force 500N, mass 25kg.

c)　Resultant Force 75N, mass 2.5kg.

Q5　**Look at** the force diagrams below and answer the questions.

a)　**Which** masses have the **same** accelerations?

b)　**Which** has the **biggest** acceleration?

c)　**Which** has the **smallest** acceleration?

Q7　A circus cannon is fired, giving Coco the Clown an acceleration of 5 m/s². He has a mass of 90kg.

a)　**What** is the size of the force that propelled Coco?

b)　**What** force is exerted on the cannon?

c)　If the cannon has a mass of 450kg, **how fast** will it accelerate, and in what direction?

Force, Mass and Acceleration

Q1   **Draw** the diagrams below showing the resultant forces. If the body is accelerating, write down the direction (up, down, right or left) in which it is accelerating.

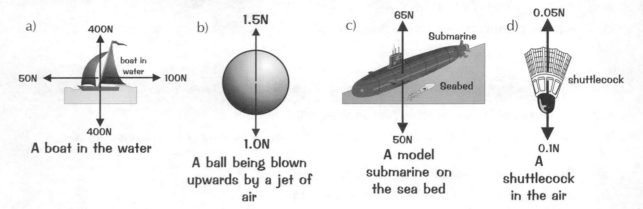

a) **400N** boat in water **50N** ← → **100N** **400N**
A boat in the water

b) **1.5N** **1.0N**
A ball being blown upwards by a jet of air

c) **65N** Submarine Seabed **50N**
A model submarine on the sea bed

d) **0.05N** shuttlecock **0.1N** **A shuttlecock in the air**

Q2   Answer TRUE or FALSE. **Explain** your answer.

a)   "If something is moving, there must be an overall force on it".

b)   "You get steady speed from balanced forces".

c)   "You get acceleration/deceleration if there is an overall force acting on an object".

d)   "The bigger the force, the smaller the acceleration".

e)   "The bigger the mass, the smaller the acceleration".

f)   "To get a small mass to accelerate as much as a big mass, it needs a bigger force".

Q3   A car of mass 2,000kg has a faulty engine which provides a driving force of 5,500N at all times. At 70 mph the drag force acting on the car is 5,400N.

a)   **Draw a diagram** for both cases (rest and at 70 mph) showing all the forces acting on the car.

b)   Find the car's acceleration when **first setting off** from rest. (Ignore the drag.)

c)   Find the car's acceleration at **70 mph**.

Q4   **Fill in the gaps** using the words below.

force   acceleration   mass   one newton   mass   double

To give a _____ of 1 kilogram an _____ of 1 metre per second squared, a force of _____ _____ is needed. Twice the _____ pushing on the same _____ would produce _____ the acceleration.

Q5   Find the **force** acting on these objects:

a)   mass 10kg, acceleration 5 m/s^2.

b)   mass 50kg, acceleration 2.5 m/s^2.

c)   mass 400kg, acceleration 8 m/s^2.

Stopping Distances for Cars

Q1   It's important to know about stopping distances if you drive a car — and if you're doing science GCSE...

a)   **Name the two distances** which make up a car's overall stopping distance.

b)   **Write the definitions** of these two distances.

Q2   Chose the correct word from each pair to complete these statements about braking force:

The greater the speed of a vehicle:

a)   The **greater / smaller** the force needed to stop it in a certain time.

b)   The **greater / smaller** the distance needed to stop it with a certain braking force.

Q3   **Fill in the gaps** in the table below

Thinking Distance (m)	Braking Distance (m)	Stopping distance (m)
8	14	
15		53
	44	61
	51	70
21		76
29	90	

Q4   This is a graph of thinking and stopping distance against speed for an average family car.

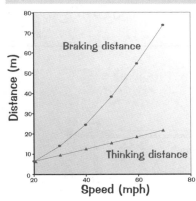

a) **Which** part of the stopping distance increases more quickly with speed?

b) **Make a copy of the graph.** Draw on curves to show how the thinking distance and braking distance would change if the same person was driving:

1)   a heavily loaded truck
2)   a sports car with brake assist.

Q5   **List** and **describe** 4 factors which affect:

a)   the thinking distance?

b)   the braking distance?

Q6   **Give examples** of everyday situations when the following factors affect braking distance. **Explain** how they do this.

a)   friction

b)   mass

c)   speed

d)   braking force.

Moments

Q1   **Draw** out the diagrams below. Mark the position of the pivot in each case.
Draw on the direction of the force needed to turn them clockwise.

a)

b)

c)

Q2   A moment is a turning force.

a)   Write down the **formula** for calculating a moment.

b)   **Describe** the two ways to increase the size of the moment.

Q3   **Calculate** the moment in each case.

a)   A man turns a car steering wheel with a force of 3N. The wheel has a radius of 25cm.

b)   A force of 8N is applied to a plank of wood 0.75m from the pivot.

c)   A cat, weighing 20N sits 120cm from the pivot of a see-saw.

Q4   **Fill in the blanks** using the words provided. Use each word once.

4   equals   equilibrium   60   clockwise   equilibrium   right   120   anticlockwise

> When a system is balanced it is in _____. The principle of moments states that
> at _____ the total _____ moment _____ the total _____ moment.
> A force of 3N, 80cm to the left of a pivot would be balanced by a force of __N, __cm
> or 2N, __cm to the _____ of the pivot.

Q5   All of these are in equilibrium. **Calculate** the missing weight or distance.
Assume the mass of the rod is negligible in each case.

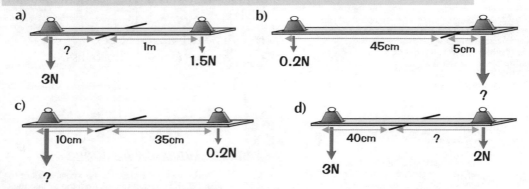

Q6   Say whether or not these systems are in **equilibrium**. If not, **which way will they turn?**

a)   A 10m long girder is suspended from its middle by a wire. A weasel weighing 30N sits at
one end of the girder. A baboon weighing 900N sits 10cm from the middle of the girder, on
the opposite side of the wire.

b)   Dexter suspends a 3N test tube from one end of a 30cm ruler, which is pivoted about its
middle. He hangs a mini ray gun weighing 4.5N on the other side of the pivot, 5cm away
from the edge of the ruler.

(Draw diagrams to help you - you should always do that in an exam)

Answers — Module BD1

Module BD1 — Supplying the Cell

Page 1 — Cells

Q1 a) 1 — ii, 2 — iii, 3 — i
  b) 1 — Nucleus, 2 — Cytoplasm, 3 — Cell membrane, 4 — Mitochondria

Q2 b) White cells have a flexible shape so that they can engulf microbes.

Q3 See diagram:

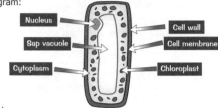

Q4 a) Chlamydomonas.
  b) Has a cell wall and a chloroplast.
  c) Nucleus, cell membrane, cytoplasm.

Q5 **i)** The shape increases the surface area for diffusion and allows the cell to bend in narrow capillaries.
  ii) Provides more space to carry haemoglobin and hence oxygen.

Q6 Virtually all plant and animal cells have a **nucleus**, cytoplasm and a **cell membrane**. Plant cells are strengthened by a cellulose **cell wall**. They also have a large, permanent **vacuole** which contains **sap**. This is a liquid that contains stored substances and water. The water provides support for the cell. Chemical processes take place in the **cytoplasm**. The **nucleus** carries genetic information. It contains chromosomes which carry genes — the genes control characteristics. Plants make their food by photosynthesis. The **palisade** cells contain many **chloroplasts** and are positioned towards the **top** of the leaf to maximise light absorption.

Page 2 — The Digestive System

Q1 Food is first broken down in the mouth. The food is chewed and shredded into smaller pieces by the teeth. This is called physical digestion.

Q2 Labelling the parts of the digestive system: A — liver, B — small intestine, C — large intestine, D — mouth and oesophagus, E — stomach, F — pancreas.

Q3 a) **Small intestine** makes protease, lipase and carbohydrase enzymes. Breakdown products of digestion are absorbed into the blood here. **Stomach** stores and squeezes food, produces hydrochloric acid and protease enzymes. **Oesophagus (gullet)** connects the mouth to the stomach. **Large intestine** absorbs water and stores faeces.
  b) Oesophagus, stomach, small intestine, large intestine.
  c) Food diffuses into the blood.

Q4) a) A is longitudinal muscle. B is circular muscle.
  b) Peristalsis.

Page 3 — The Digestive System

Q5 An enzyme is a substance which acts as a biological catalyst. Enzymes are proteins that will only catalyse certain reactions, and work best over a narrow range of temperature and pH.

Q6 Chemical digestion is the process in which large food molecules are broken down into smaller molecules which can be absorbed into the blood. Digestive enzymes are the biological catalysts that speed up the process.

Q7 Glucose, amino acids, fatty acids and glycerol are smaller molecules which can diffuse into the blood, whereas the original molecules are too large.

Q8 a) Hydrochloric acid.
  b) Hydrochloric acid kills most of the microbes taken in with the food. It also provides the correct pH for the protease enzymes there to work effectively.

c) The pH of the stomach contents is about pH 2. Hydrochloric acid is a strong acid so you would expect a low pH.

Q9 a) Emulsify means to break down droplets of liquid into smaller droplets, allowing the smaller droplets to spread through another liquid in which they cannot dissolve.
  b) The surface area of fat increases when it is emulsified.
  c) Bile emulsifies fats. This provides a larger surface area for lipase enzymes to work on, increasing the rate of digestion.

Q10 a) Bile neutralises the acid that was added to food in the stomach.
  b) This provides alkaline conditions in which enzymes in the small intestine work most effectively.

Q11 a) A higher temperature will increase enzyme activity up to an optimum level. If the temperature increases too far then the activity decreases.
  b)

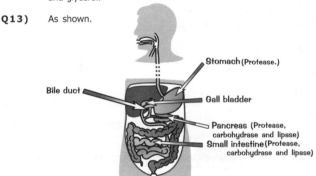

c) Very high temperature or an extreme level of pH irreversibly damages (denatures) the enzyme, and its activity falls rapidly. At temperatures above 45°C, the enzymes stop working as shown by the graph.

Page 4 — The Digestive System

Q12 Starch is digested to form smaller molecules called sugars. Protein is digested to form smaller molecules called amino acids.
Fat is digested to form smaller molecules called fatty acids and glycerol.

Q13) As shown.

Q14 a) The products of digestion are absorbed into the bloodstream in the small intestine.
  b) Excess water is absorbed in the large intestine.
  c) If too much water is absorbed, the faeces become hard, causing constipation.
  d) If too little water is absorbed, the faeces become very soft, causing diarrhoea.

Page 5 — Lungs and Breathing

Q1 The breathing system takes **air** into and out of the body. This allows **oxygen** to pass from the air into the bloodstream, and **carbon dioxide** to pass out of the bloodstream into the air.

Q2 a) The heart would normally be found in the space at X.
  b) Matching letters to labels.

Letter	Label
A	Trachea
B	Lung
C	Diaphragm
D	Bronchus
E	Bronchiole
F	Alveoli
G	Rib

Answers — Module BD1

Q3 a) The ribs form the rib cage which protects the lungs from external damage.
b) The diaphragm separates the lungs from the abdomen.
c) Bronchi and bronchioles contain rigid cartilage which keeps the tubes open in low pressure.

Q4 Correct order : trachea → bronchi → bronchioles → alveoli.

Q5 a) The trachea is also called the windpipe.
b) There is one bronchus for each lung (so two bronchi in total).
c) A bronchiole is a smaller air passage formed when the bronchi divide. The bronchioles themselves divide further producing smaller and smaller bronchioles.
d) An alveolus is a tiny air sac found at the end of bronchioles, where gas exchange occurs.

Page 6 — Lungs and Breathing

Q6 The alveoli provide an enormous surface area over which diffusion can take place. The walls are moist, allowing gases to dissolve so that they can diffuse through the walls of the alveoli. There is a dense network of capillaries surrounding the alveoli. The walls of the capillaries are also only one cell thick, and gases can diffuse easily through them into and out of the bloodstream.

Q7 The intercostal muscles contract.
This pulls the ribcage upwards.
The intercostal and diaphragm muscles contract.
This causes the diaphragm to flatten.
These two movements cause an increase in the volume of the thorax.
Consequently the pressure in the thorax decreases.
Atmospheric air enters the lungs.

Q8 When we breathe out the ribcage moves down and the diaphragm moves up. These two movements cause a decrease in the volume of the thorax and the consequent increase in pressure results in air being forced out of the lungs.

Page 7 — Diffusion

Q1 In order they appear: spreading, higher, lower.

Q2 In the diagram, oxygen is diffusing from the alveolus into the blood. Carbon dioxide is diffusing from the blood into the alveolus.

Q3 a) When the blood reaches the body cells, oxygen is released from the oxyhaemoglobin in the red blood cells and diffuses into the body cells.
b) Carbon dioxide diffuses into the plasma in blood and is carried back to the lungs.

Q4 The villi greatly increase the surface area for absorbing food inside the small intestine. They also have a very thin layer of cells and a good blood supply which assist quick absorption.

Page 8 — The Circulatory System

Q1 a) One goes to the lungs and the other goes to all other organs of the body.
b) Blood can be pumped around the body at higher pressure, so the cells receive more oxygen.
c) Two systems are needed because one receives deoxygenated blood from the body and just pumps it to the lungs. The other receives oxygenated blood from the lungs and pumps it round the whole body.

Q2 a) 5 from nutrients, oxygen, waste, hormones, water and antibodies.
b) The two main components are the heart and blood vessels.

Q3 a) The heart has 4 chambers.
b) The upper chambers are called the atria.
The lower chambers are called the ventricles.

Q4 a) 1 - right atrium
2 - right ventricle
3 - left atrium
4 - left ventricle
b) Most of the wall of the heart is made from muscle fibre. This is expected because the heart works by contracting and

relaxing which is what muscles do.
c) A - semi-lunar valve
B - bicuspid (mitral) valve
C - semi-lunar valve
D - tricuspid valve

Q5 Blood enters an **atrium** of the heart. The atrium **contracts** and forces blood into a **ventricle**. The **ventricle contracts** and forces blood **out** of the heart. **Valves** in the heart ensure that the blood flows in the **correct** direction.

Page 9 — Blood Vessels

Q1 Arteries: Carry blood from the heart, at high pressure and have a narrower lumen and thicker walls.
Veins: Carry blood to the heart, at low pressure and have a bigger lumen and thinner walls.

Q2 a) A — Endothelium.
B — Elastic fibres and smooth muscle.
C — Fibrous coat.
D — Lumen.
b) Similarities: Both vessels have a lumen surrounded by an endothelium, elastic fibres and smooth muscles, and a fibrous coat.
Differences: For a given diameter of blood vessel, arteries have a narrower lumen and thicker walls than veins do.
c) Arteries must carry blood at high pressure. The thick, muscular and elastic walls allow them to stand up to the high pressures produced by the heart. They can return to their original diameter after the surge of blood at high pressure. Veins only need to carry blood at low pressure. They do not need such thick walls, but the large lumen helps to maintain the blood flow.

Q3 a) & d)

Vein   Artery

b) The valve prevents blood flowing backwards.
c) Valves can also be found in the heart.
d) Arrow added to diagram of vein as above: blood flowing from left to right in the diagram pushes the walls of the valve against the wall of the capillary; if blood tries to flow back the other way, it fills the two halves of the valve with blood so closing it tightly.

Q4 a) 1 - Endothelium, 2 - Lumen, 3 - Nucleus of cell
b) Capillaries allow cells to receive the substances they need from the blood, including water, oxygen and dissolved nutrients. They also allow cells to pass waste products into the blood, including carbon dioxide and other excretory products.
c) The wall of the capillary is very thin, often just one cell thick. This allows substances to pass into the cells from the blood, and out of the cells into the blood quickly.

Page 10 — Blood

Q1 Completed summary:

Red cells	Platelets	White cells	Plasma
Transport of oxygen	Helping to clot blood at the site of a wound	Protection of the body from infection by: engulfing microbes, producing antibodies, producing antitoxins	Transport of red cells, white cells, platelets, dissolved mineral salts, products of digestion, carbon dioxide, urea, water, antibodies, antitoxins, hormones

Q2 Red blood cell.

Q3 In the lungs, **haemoglobin** combines with **oxygen** to form **oxyhaemoglobin**. In other organs, **oxyhaemoglobin** splits up into **haemoglobin** and **oxygen**.

Q4 **White** blood cells help to protect the body against disease. They have a **flexible** shape, as this lets them **engulf** micro-organisms. **Antibodies** are produced to fight the **micro-organisms**. Bacteria produce harmful toxins, but

Answers — Modules BD1 and BD2

these are countered by **antitoxins** carried by the **plasma** in blood

Q 5 Plasma transports all of the listed substances, with the exception of oxygen (transported by the red cells).

Q 6 Platelets help in the clotting of blood at the site of a wound. This prevents blood loss and entry of micro-organisms into the body.

BD2 — Control in Animals and Plants

Page 11 — The Nervous System

Q 1 a) Matching sense organs to senses:

Sense organ	nose	tongue	ears	eyes	skin
Sense	smell	taste	hearing/balance	sight	temperature/touch

b) Matching sense organs to stimuli:

Stimulus	chemicals	light	position	sound	pressure	temperature change
Sense	smell/taste	sight	balance	hearing	touch	temperature

c) Completed table:

Sense organ	Stimulus	Sense
nose	chemicals	smell
tongue	chemicals	taste
eyes	light	sight
ears	sound	hearing
	position	balance
skin	pressure	touch
	temperature change	temperature

Q 2 a) Stimuli. Singular: stimulus.
b) Receptors.
c) If we can detect and respond to changes in the environment we can, for example, avoid danger and find food.

Q 3 a) X: brain Y: spinal cord Z: nerves/neurones.
b) The central nervous system.
c) Nerve impulses can travel in both directions in the spinal cord, but remember that they can only travel in one direction in individual nerve fibres.
d) Functions of the brain: to receive impulses from all the sensory organs in the body; to send off motor impulses to glands and muscles; to correlate impulses from various sensory neurones; to coordinate activities in the body; to store information. The brain is not involved in reflex actions. These continue without involving the brain, but there may be connection to the brain to allow us to sense that we have, for example, moved our leg in response to a tap on the knee.

Q 4 Electrical impulses pass from a receptor along a **sensory neurone** to the spinal cord or brain. They then pass along a **motor neurone** to a muscle or gland. The muscle or gland brings about the **response**.

Page 12 — Neurones and Reflexes

Q 1 The cells are called neurones.

Q 2 a) A sensory neurone carries a nerve impulse from a receptor to the spinal cord. A motor neurone carries a nerve impulse from the spinal cord to the effector, eg. muscle.
b) Diagram B represents a sensory neurone. There is a sensory nerve ending on the left, and the cell body is attached to the nerve fibre, rather than being at one end.
c)

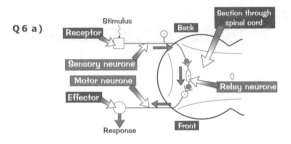

d) Motor neurone: X is connected to an effector, such as a

muscle or gland.
Sensory neurone: X is connected to a connector (relay) neurone.

e) Key features: Long nerve fibres (axons) to connect distant parts of the body. Many branching nerve endings to make many connections with other nerves or with muscles and glands.

Q 3 A reflex action is an **automatic** response to a **stimulus**. It happens very **quickly** and **does not involve** the **brain**. Reflex actions allow us to coordinate body activity by nervous control.

Q 4 a) The stimulus is the heat of the hot object.
b) The response is the movement of the finger.
c) The effector is the arm muscle.

Page 13 — Neurones and Reflexes

Q 5 Impulses from a receptor pass along a sensory neurone to the central nervous system; at a junction (synapse) between a sensory neurone and a relay neurone in the central nervous system, a chemical is released which causes an impulse to be sent along a relay neurone; a chemical is released at the synapse between a relay neurone and a motor neurone in the central nervous system. This causes impulses to be sent along a motor neurone to the organ (the effector) which brings about the response; the effector is either a muscle or a gland; a muscle responds by contracting, a gland by releasing (secreting) chemical substances.

Q 6 a)

b) The sensory neurone detects the stimulus. The relay neurone connects the sensory and motor neurones. The motor neurones passes the signal to the effector.
c) Correct reflex arc: stimulus → receptor→ neurones (coordinator) → effector → response.
d) The reflex arc shows that nerve impulses from a reflex action do not have to pass through the brain. Therefore reflex actions are involuntary and much quicker.

Q 7 Tap on leg → stretch receptor → impulse passes along sensory neurone → impulse passes through relay neurone → impulse passes along motor neurone → leg muscle contracts → leg straightens.
Grit in eye → touch receptor in eyelid → impulse passes along sensory neurone → impulse passes through relay neurone → impulse passes through motor neurone → tears secreted by tear gland in eye → eyes water to remove grit.

Page 14 — The Eye

Q 1 Completed table:

Label	Name
A	Suspensory ligaments
B	Iris
C	Cornea
D	Pupil
E	Lens
F	Ciliary muscles
G	Retina
H	Sclera
I	Optic nerve

Q 2 Correct part and function:
Ciliary muscles — pull the lens for focusing.
Cornea — lets light into the eye and begins focusing.
Iris — controls the amount of light entering the eye.

Answers — Module BD2

Lens — focuses light onto the retina.
Optic nerve — sends signals to the brain.
Pupil — lets light through to the lens.
Retina — light-sensitive layer - sends signals to the optic nerve.
Suspensory ligaments — holds the lens in place.

Q 3 a) Light enters through the cornea.
b) The cornea and lens then produce an image on the retina.
c) The receptor cells in the retina send impulses to the brain along sensory neurones in the optic nerve.
d) To focus on nearby objects, the ciliary muscles contract which slackens the suspensory ligaments and the lens becomes fat.

Q 4 a) The black circle at the centre of the iris is the pupil.
b) Muscle A: radial muscles; Muscle B: circular muscles.
c) Diagram 2 shows the eye in bright light. This is because the pupil is very small, restricting the amount of light entering the lens.
d) In diagram 1, the circular muscles are relaxed, and the radial muscles have contracted.
e) In diagram 2, the radial muscles are relaxed, and the circular muscles have contracted.
f) In bright light, the circular muscles of the iris contract and the radial muscles relax. This makes the diameter of the pupil smaller, allowing less light through to the lens. In dim light, the radial muscles contract and the circular muscles relax. The diameter of the pupil increases allowing more light in.
g) Other muscles involved with the eye include the ciliary muscles. These pull the lens to allow focusing. Extrinsic muscles move the eyeball around in the eye socket.

Page 15 — Hormones

Q 1

Name of hormone	Gland	Function
a) Insulin	Pancreas	turns glucose to glycogen
b) Oestrogen, progesterone	Ovaries	develops female sexual characteristics
c) Follicle Stimulating Hormone (FSH)	Pituitary	causes eggs to mature and ovaries to produce oestrogen
d) Growth hormone	Pituitary	controls growth
e) Thyroxine	Thyroid	controls the metabolism
f) Adrenaline	Adrenal	prepare the body for flight or fight situations
g) Testosterone	Testes	develops male sexual characteristics

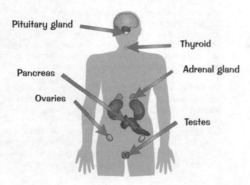

Q 2 In this order. Adrenal gland, increase, towards, liver.

Q 3 Males — voice breaks, hair grows on face and body, more muscular body, genitals develop, sperm production.
Females — breasts develop, hips widen, periods start, pubic hair, and hair under arms grows.

Q 4

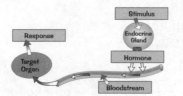

Page 16 — Hormones

Q 5 A very high blood sugar level can cause coma and death.

Q 6 a) Insulin
b) The pancreas
c) Treated by careful attention to diet and by injecting insulin into the blood.
d) See graph: The lack of insulin would mean that the glucose levels would continue to rise.

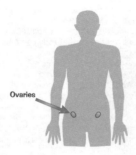

Q 7 When the concentration is too high, the pancreas secretes insulin into the blood. This stimulates the liver into converting glucose into insoluble glycogen to store it.

Q 8 1 — C, 2 — D, 3 — A, 4 — E, 5 — B.

Q 9 Anabolic steroids are based upon testosterone and stimulate muscle growth, which helps the athlete to increase his performance.

Page 17 — Hormones

Q10 a) Progesterone and oestrogen (or just progesterone.)
b) It would increase it.
c) Egg development and release would be stopped.
d) Yes. Levels of the hormones would fall back to normal after a period of time.

Q11 a) Oestrogen and progesterone are produced in the ovaries.
b) See picture.

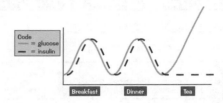

Q12 a) FSH.
b) It causes more eggs to mature.

Q13 Oestrogen — Stops production of FSH, causes the lining of the uterus to thicken and the release of an egg on day 14. Progesterone — Maintains the lining of the uterus. When the level of progesterone falls, the lining breaks down.

Page 18 — Hormones

Q14 a) A is progesterone, B is oestrogen.
b) As shown below

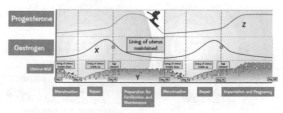

c) FSH

Answers — Modules BD2 and BD3

Q15a) Oestrogen
b) Progesterone

Q16a) FSH
b) Oestrogen
c) High levels of FSH can result in difficult and dangerous multiple births. The high levels of FSH stimulate production of oestrogen, if oestrogen levels get too high then natural production of FSH is hampered and will eventually stop.

Page 19 — Plant Hormones

Q1 a) i) Down.
ii) The bottom cells are inhibited by the accumulation of auxin.
iii) Gravity and moisture + light.
b) i) Up.
ii) Bottom cells elongate faster due to the accumulation of auxin.
iii) Gravity and light.

Q2 a) Grow them in the dark / cover the tip of the shoot / give them an equal amount of light all the way round (and it would help to plant them upright).
b) The shoots are getting more light from the left. He should block off all the light/give them even light/cover the tip.

Q3 a) First and second plants grow straight, third grows towards the light, fourth grows straight and taller than the others, and will also look less healthy.
b) First and second get an even amount of light/hormones evenly affected; in the third, light causes the hormone to accumulate on the left. In fourth, no growth hormone is destroyed by the light, so plant grows faster (but would be thinner).

Q4 a) Mr. Tomavitch would take cuttings from his plants. Normally, they wouldn't grow, but by adding rooting compound, which is a plant growth hormone, they will produce roots rapidly and start growing as new plants. In this way, he can produce lots of clones of a good plant really quickly which increases his productivity.
b) Being able to control when his tomatoes ripen means that Mr. Tomavitch can pick them when they're still unripe (and therefore firmer and less easily damaged). He can then spray them with ripening hormone so they will ripen on the way to the supermarket and be perfect just as they reach the shelves.

Q5 **Rooting hormone** is a substance which is applied to the soil around the roots of a cutting. It causes roots to rapidly grow from the cutting, so lots of copies of a particular plant can quickly be made. **Selective weedkillers** are sprayed over broad-leaved weed plants. They disrupt the growth patterns of the weeds, which kills them without harming the surrounding plants. **Growth regulator** is applied to flower buds before they have flowered. This stops the flower bud from flowering whilst it is being transported.

Module BD3 — Ecology

Page 20 — Population and Habitat

Q1 a) You aim the collection tube at the animal and then suck on the mouthpiece and the animal goes into the container.

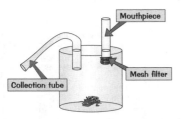

b) You can use the net to catch flying insects and small aquatic creatures.
c) The animal gets attracted to the food and crawls under the cover and into the jar. The cover makes sure the rain doesn't get in to drown the animal.

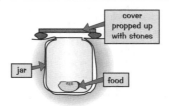

d) Quadrats are a 1m² square frame that you place on the floor and count everything in its area.

Q2) 60500 grass plants, 22000 buttercups, 8250 clovers, 5500 daisies, 2200 stag beetles.
1. Take a larger sample for a more accurate set of results.
2. The sample may not accurately represent the population. It's better to take more samples and take them from different areas of the field.

Q3 Predators are animals which kill and eat other animals. Prey are the animals eaten by predators. Examples could include foxes (predators) eat rabbits (prey), owl eats mouse etc.

Q4 Possible table:

Factor	Examples
Competition for water	Weeds and wheat
Competition for light	Trees and grass
Competition for nutrients	Sycamore and oak trees
Competition for food	Blackbirds and thrushes
Competition for space	Weeds and carrots
Predation	Mice eaten by owls
Grazing	Grass eaten by cows
Amount of food available	Mice for owls to eat
Disease	Myxomatosis in rabbits

Q5 The sidewinder's movements help to keep it cool by keeping most of its body off the hot sand. Different parts of the body are in contact at different times as it moves. It also allows the sidewinder to get a grip in the sand.

Q6 Burrows are likely to be cool during the day, allowing the animals to come out at night when it is cooler on the surface. Prey will be hidden from predators (and predators will be hidden from their prey). As it is cooler underground, the animals may be able to conserve moisture. However, it is unlikely that there will be any food in the burrow, and the animals will need to forage at night. It may be difficult to find food in the dark, and predators may be hunting then too.

Q7 a) The plants are able to continue their species without trying to grow when there is insufficient water.
b) The plants can reach down to where there may still be water/ minerals.
c) The roots can absorb surface water, e.g. if there is light rain or early morning dew.
d) Plants can continue to live even when there is no ground water.
e) Leaves are a potential source of water loss through transpiration, and so water can be conserved this way.
f) Water can be lost by transpiration through stomata. This is reduced if the stomata are only open at night when it is cooler.
g) The thorns put off grazing animals that might try to eat the plants or get at their stored water.

Q8 Lemmings have fur and live in burrows to reduce their heat loss. Their rounded bodies will keep their surface area to volume ratio down to reduce heat loss. Their ears are small and hidden by fur which again reduces heat loss. Their fur is light brown for camouflage in the tundra. They can hide from predators in their burrows.

Page 21 — Population and Habitat

Q1 a) There are extremes of temperature in the Arctic; it can be quite warm in summer, but the temperature is below freezing for most of the year. The dark winter means that winter temperatures are always low. There can be strong winds, which would make it seem much colder. There is relatively little rainfall, with most falling in the summer, so it is quite dry.

Answers — Module BD3

b) Plants grow close to the ground to withstand the strong winds. Their small leaves will reduce water loss.

c) The cold will be a major problem in the Arctic, and adaptations such as fur and lots of fat can be expected. Dark animals would be easily visible against the white snow. White fur would provide camouflage for both predators and prey. Animals may also live in burrows to escape the cold and strong winds. Grazing animals might find it difficult to find food if the plants are low growing with small leaves.

Q2 a) Aids heat loss.
b) The desert is very dry. Being able to hold lots of water prevents dehydration.
c) Not sweating and not producing much urine reduces water loss.
d) Sandy colour helps camouflage the camel.
e) Large feet spread the weight of the camel and stop it sinking into the soft sand.
f) Having no layer of body fat helps the camel to lose body heat, which helps it as the desert is hot.
g) Tolerating big changes in its body temperature means the camel doesn't need to sweat. This prevents dehydration.

Q3 Any three from: It is strong, agile and fast, which helps it catch prey; Strong jaws and sharp teeth for killing prey; Good stereo vision with both eyes facing forwards, which helps it to find prey; Camouflaged body for stalking prey. It has the right sort of teeth for chewing meat.

Q4 Any three from temperature, amount of light, availability of water, availability of oxygen and availability of carbon dioxide.

Page 22 — Population and Habitat

Q1 Plants — space, water, nutrients from soil.
Animals — space, water and food

Q2 a) Fast and agile, so can escape from predators.
b) Brown colour camouflages the bunny.
c) Good all-round vision helps it spot predators.
d) Good hearing helps it hear predators.
e) Other rabbits can see the bright white tail when the rabbit is running.

Q3 The polar bear's surface is kept to a **minimum** compared to its body weight. This **reduces** heat loss. It has a **thick** layer of blubber for **insulation**. Its fur is greasy so it **sheds** water after swimming to **prevent** cooling due to evaporation. It has **white** fur for **camouflage** and is a **powerful runner** which helps it catch **prey** on land.

Page 23 — Food Chains and Pyramids

Q1 Both organisms gain from a mutualistic relationship. Root nodules in leguminous plants contain nitrogen-fixing bacteria which provide the plant with the nitrogen it needs. In turn the plant supplies the bacteria with the nutrients they need.

Q2

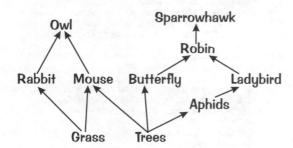

Q3 a) A pyramid of numbers shows the numbers of organisms at each trophic level in a food chain.
b) Row F is the most likely to represent the numbers of organisms.
c) The size of the organism increases going from left to right along this food chain.
d) Pyramid A.

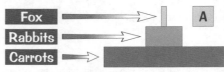

e) The larger the organism, the narrower its bar.

Q4 a)

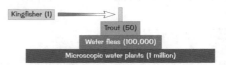

b)

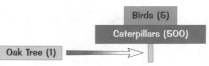

c) It is not always possible to draw the bars to scale because the numbers at each level can be very different. For example, it the kingfisher bar was 1mm wide, the microscopic water plants bar would be 1km wide!
d) A pyramid of numbers can have a non-pyramid shape if there is a single, large producer.
e) & f)

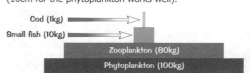

Similar to answer for **d)**, the parasites survive off a single large producer — a human.
g) Any suitable non-pyramidal example with relevant labelling and explanation.

Page 24 — Food Chains and Pyramids

Q1 Biomass is the mass of living organisms at a particular trophic level. Pyramids of biomass show the mass of living organisms at each trophic level in a food chain.

Q2 a) Pyramid:
(10cm for the phytoplankton works well).

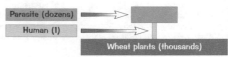

b) If the biomass of the lowest trophic level is very large compared to the top level, a scale drawing will need a bar that is too small to draw accurately. A vertical line can be used then.
c) The most mass is lost zooplankton → small fish (70kg).
d) The greatest proportion is lost small fish → cod (90%).
e) Biomass is lost through waste materials and nutrients used for respiration.
f) 1kg of dry cod would eat 10kg of dry small fish.
Since both fish have the same proportion of water in their bodies, 1kg of wet cod would eat 10kg of wet small fish.
so 7.5kg of wet cod would eat 75kg of wet small fish.
So 1 cod would eat 75 ÷ 1.5 = 50 small fish

Q3 a) Pyramid A — A large producer could support many herbivores, which then support fewer carnivores. The first bar is small.
b) Pyramid B — Pyramids of biomass have the proper pyramid shape.
c) Pyramid D — Parasites are smaller than their hosts, so there will more of them, giving a wider final bar.
d) Pyramids B or D — The bottom bar would be the largest because many algae would be needed.

Q4 The mass of living material at each stage of a food chain is **less** than it was at the stage below. This means pyramids of **biomass** get **narrower** the higher you go. This is not always the case with pyramids of **numbers**.

Answers — Module BD3

Page 25 — Food Chains and Pyramids

Q1   5, 8000kg

Q2 a)   Producers – green plants.
    b)   Photosynthesis.
    c)   It decreases.

Q3   He should grow vegetables, wheat and other crops that can be eaten by humans. This is because material and energy is lost at each stage in a food chain. This means that the efficiency of food production can be improved by reducing the number of stages in food chains.

Q4 a)   Energy and materials are always lost in organisms' waste materials. Organisms use energy for respiration.
    b)   Much of the energy loss in **respiration** occurs as **heat** loss to the environment. This loss is **very** high in mammals and birds. Their bodies must be kept at a **constant** temperature, which is usually **higher** than that of their environment.
    c)   The goldfish is cold blooded, so doesn't have to use energy regulating its body temperature. The gerbil does, so it needs more energy, therefore more food.
    d)   10%

Q5 a)   They don't use energy moving or lose much energy through heat loss to their surroundings. This means they require less energy to live, so don't require as much food. This makes farming them cheaper.
    b)   Hormones are used to regulate the ripening of fruit on the plant and during transport to consumers. This decreases the amount of fruit that goes bad before it gets to consumers, so the amount of wastage is reduced.
    c)   Advantage: Cost of food production is reduced, so food is cheaper for shoppers. Disadvantage of battery farming: The warm, crowded conditions in which the chickens are kept help the spread of disease. The chickens have to be given lots of antibiotics to keep them healthy. Disadvantage of adding hormones to fruit: Hormones may be harmful to humans.

Page 26 — Decomposition

Q1 a)   For growth and other life processes.
    b)   In animal waste materials or through the decomposition of dead plant and animal material.
    c)   So plants have the materials they need to grow and live.

Q2 a)   Decomposers.
    b)   The bacteria and fungi obtain nutrients for respiration, and for growth and repair.
    c)   Carbon dioxide.
    d)   Minerals and nitrogen compounds.
    e)   Bacteria and fungi decompose dead animals and plants, releasing valuable minerals and nutrients from them. These minerals and nutrients are vital for the healthy growth of plants (without plants, the carbon cycle would cease).

Q3 a)   warm
    b)   moist
    c)   plenty of

Q4 a)   To decompose the sewage.
    b)   Decomposing microorganisms there need plenty of oxygen.
    c)   The decomposed material in compost is full of the nutrients that plants need to grow.

Q5   Processes which return materials to the environment.

Page 27 — The Carbon Cycle

Q1 a)   Photosynthesis.
    b)   Respiration.
    c)   Clockwise from top: carbon dioxide, photosynthesis, carbon, respiration.
    d)   Fats, proteins and carbohydrates.

Q2 a)   It becomes part of the fats and proteins in the animals' body.
    b)   Respiration.

Q3   When plants and animals die, some animals and microorganisms feed on their bodies. Carbon is released into the atmosphere as carbon dioxide when these organisms respire.

Q4   **Carbon dioxide** is removed from the atmosphere by **green** plants for photosynthesis. Some is returned by **respiration**. The carbon is used to make **fats**, **carbohydrates** and **proteins** which make up the 'body' of the plants. Animals get carbon by **eating** plants , and return some carbon dioxide to the atmosphere when they respire. Dead plant and animal material is **decomposed** by **microorganisms**. More carbon dioxide is returned to the environment when they **respire**.

Page 28 — The Nitrogen Cycle

Q1 a)   They absorb nitrates in the soil.
    b)   Making proteins.
    c)   Making proteins.
    d)   Eating plants.

Q2 a)   Putrefying bacteria.
    b)   Ammonium compounds.
    c)   Nitrifying bacteria convert ammonium compounds to nitrates.

Q3   Some is used when plants respire, some is used when animals respire, some is used when the decomposing bacteria respire and some is present in the nitrates returned to the soil.

Q4 a)   False — they get it as nitrates from the soil.
    b)   False — they return carbon dioxide.
    c)   True
    d)   True
    e)   False — they need it to make proteins.
    f)   False — putrefying bacteria do this.
    g)   True.
    h)   False — they get it from eating plants.

Page 29 — The Carbon and Nitrogen Cycles

Q1   Clockwise from top: nitrates in soil, animals eat plants, animal protein, death and decay, nitrifying bacteria.

Q2   First column: Plants absorb nitrates and when they die they are decomposed to leave ammonium compounds, among other things. Also animals eat plants and produce waste. The waste contains ammonium compounds and when animals decompose they leave ammonium compounds as well. Second column: Nitrifying bacteria convert ammonium compounds to nitrates in the soil.

Q3 a)   Sewage works and compost heaps.
    b)   Warm.
    c)   Fats, carbohydrates, proteins would all do.
    d)   Photosynthesis.
    e)   The microorganisms that do the decomposing release carbon dioxide into the atmosphere when they respire.
    f)   Nitrifying bacteria.
    g)   Proteins.

Page 30 — Our Effect on The Environment

Q1   Building, quarrying, farming, dumping waste.

Q2   Air: sulphur dioxide, carbon dioxide, nitrogen oxides.
Land: pesticides, herbicides.
Water: sewage, fertiliser, pesticides, herbicides.

Q3 i)   Cutting down trees will increase the amount of carbon dioxide in the atmosphere as it reduces the amount removed and "locked up" as wood.
    ii)   If the trees are burnt then carbon dioxide will be released into the atmosphere.
    ii)   If they aren't burnt they'll be left to rot, in which case they provide food for microorganisms which will respire more and so produce more carbon dioxide.

Q4 a)   The rate of use of raw materials in increasing along with the size of the population.
    b)   They are in danger of running out as we use them quicker and quicker.
    c)   Larger as from the graph we can see there are roughly 6 times as many people alive now as there were 200 years ago, so the effects of our actions are going to be larger.
    d)   More waste is being produced now, so it is important that it is handled properly, as more pollution will be caused if it is not.

Q5 a)   Carbon dioxide.

Answers — Modules BD3 and CD1

b) Two reasons, 1: it has increased the release of carbon dioxide (due to the burning and rotting of the felled trees) 2: It has reduced the rate at which carbon dioxide is removed from the atmosphere and 'locked up' as wood.

c) Burning them will produce sulphur dioxide and nitrogen oxides and these gases are the cause of acid rain.

d) There are limited supplies of fossil fuels and as the population grows we need more and more energy. So unless we have other energy sources we will run out of fossil fuels and have no way to make energy.

Q6 a) Developed   **b)** Developing

Page 31 — Pollution

Q1 a) "Development that meets the needs of today's population without harming the ability of future generations to meet their own needs." Mmm, sounds good.

b) Without it the human race may have problems in the future caused by its actions in the present.

c) Fish quotas prevent too many fish being taken and as old trees are felled new trees are planted.

d) Population size, waste products and food and energy demands. These all must be monitored so as not to cause too much disruption to the environment.

Q2 a) By replacing the nutrients which crops remove from the soil.
b) It will be washed into the river.
c) Eutrophication.

Q3 a) Correct sequence: Excess fertilisers leach from the soil and are washed into the lake.
There is increased competition between the plants, and some die as a result.
Water plants in the lake start to grow rapidly.
The number of microbes that feed on dead organisms increases.
The microbes take more oxygen from the water for their respiration.
Fish and other aquatic animals die from lack of oxygen.

b) The plants grow more quickly because they have received additional nitrates and phosphates.

c) The plants are likely to be competing for light and space. Nitrates, phosphates and water are likely to be in excess.

d) The oxygen content of the water goes down because additional decomposer microbes use the oxygen to respire.

e) In a eutrophic lake, nitrates are not limited because they're being added to the community from outside. Eutrophication kills animals and eventually plants. Therefore, the microbes are not recycling the nutrients but causing increasing death followed by yet more decay.

Q4 a) Predators are introduced to eat pests
b) Advantages: You don't have to use potentially harmful pesticides. The predators reproduce, so you don't have to keep putting more in. Disadvantages: It takes a long time to work and may have unforeseen effects on food chains.

Q5 a) The red kite used to be hunted as they were considered a pest because they kept killing other birds and animals. The red squirrel couldn't handle all the competition from the North American grey squirrel. The osprey wasn't getting enough fish because of competition from fishermen and also the Victorians collected osprey eggs.

b) Conservation organisations such as the RSPB can educate people to preserve the habitats of endangered species. Land providing a good habitat can be bought and maintained. Conservation organisations can monitor the health and welfare of communities of endangered species. Legislation is the final, more extreme solution.

c) Because there is less impact on the environment so population numbers are likely to rise.

CD1 — Equations and Rates of Reaction

Page 32 — Chemical Equations

Q1 a)
NaCl: Na-1, Cl-1;
$MgCO_3$: Mg-1, C-1, O-3;
H_2: H-2;
KOH: K-1, O-1, H-1;
$Ca(OH)_2$: Ca-1, O-2, H-2;
b) compound, compound, element, compound, compound

c)
NaCl:	2
$MgCO_3$:	5
H_2:	2
KOH:	3
$Ca(OH)_2$:	5

d) Sodium Chloride.
Magnesium Carbonate.
Hydrogen.
Potassium Hydroxide.
Calcium Hydroxide.

Q2 a) calcium carbonate → calcium oxide + carbon dioxide

b) magnesium oxide + hydrochloric acid → magnesium chloride + water

c) sulphur dioxide + oxygen → sulphur trioxide

d) sodium carbonate + nitric acid → sodium nitrate + water + carbon dioxide

e) nitrogen + hydrogen → ammonia

Q3 a) $CaCO_3 \rightarrow CaO + O_2$
b) $MgO + 2HCl \rightarrow MgCl_2 + H_2O$
c) $2SO_2 + O_2 \rightarrow 2SO_3$
d) $Na_2CO_3 + 2HNO_3 \rightarrow 2NaNO_3 + H_2O + CO_2$
e) $N_2 + 3H_2 \rightarrow 2NH_3$

Q4 a) (i) Mg-1, O-2
Na-1, Cl-2
Ca-1, Cl-2
Na-1; H-2, O-1
K-1, N-1, O-3

(ii) Mg-1, O-1
Na-1, Cl-1
Ca-1, Cl-2
Na-1, O-1, H-1; H-2
K-1, N-1, O-2; O-2

b) $2Mg + O_2 \rightarrow 2MgO$
$2Na + Cl_2 \rightarrow 2NaCl$
$Ca + Cl_2 \rightarrow CaCl_2$
$2Na + 2H_2O \rightarrow 2NaOH + H_2$
$2KNO_3 \rightarrow 2KNO_2 + O_2$

Page 33 — Rates of Reaction

Q1 Match, egg, digestion, concrete, rust.

Q2 Catalysts are used up in reactions - false; catalysts are specific to certain reactions - true; enzymes are biological catalysts - true; reactions slow if catalysts are used - false; enzymes increase the activation energy - false; reactions will speed up if they are heated - true; usually only small quantities of catalyst are needed - true; increasing concentration increases the rate of reaction - true; pressure increases the rate of gaseous reactions - true; reactions are faster initially, then slow down - true.

Q3 heating the acid, using more conc. acid, using powdered metal not ribbon, using a catalyst, shaking the flask also works because it keeps the magnesium in contact with the acid.

Q4 Reacting magnesium with sulphuric acid, using a gas syringe to measure the amount of hydrogen given off etc.

Q5 Marble chips reacting with hydrochloric acid. The mass of the reaction vessel contents can be measured and seen to change as CO_2 escapes.

Q6

Particles miss each other	A glancing collision	A head-on collision

Page 34 — Rates of Reaction

Q1 a&b)

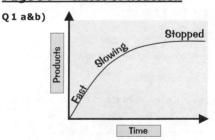

c) Reaction: start, middle, end
Speed: fast, slowing, stopped

Answers — Module CD1

Page 35 — Rates of Reaction

Q 1 a) Higher temperature means a faster reaction.
b) **(1)** 8cm³/10s = 0.8cm³/s **(2)** 16cm³/10s = 1.6cm³/s
(3) 32cm³/10s = 3.2cm³/s
c) A 10 °C rise in temperature doubles the rate of reaction
d) No.

Q 2 a) i) B **ii)** C **iii)** A **iv)** D
b) i) More product formed as there are more ions in the acid to react (magnesium was previously in excess).
ii) Same rate as the amount of particles in a certain volume is the same, so the collision rate will be the same. However there is more acid so assuming there are sufficient marble chips there will be a greater volume of gas produced.
iii) A larger surface area due to the smaller particles means there are more particles available for a collision and so available to react. The same amount of product is formed.
iv) Acid is colder so particles will have less kinetic energy giving a lower average speed of particles. This means that there will be a smaller number of collisions and of that number a smaller proportion will be able to provide the energy needed to overcome the activation energy barrier.

Page 36 — Collision Theory

Q 1 Collide; energy; collision theory; concentration; catalyst.

Q 2 a) Faster; more often; energy; faster.
b) Particles; faster.
c) Surface area; faster.
d) Moderate; successful; collision; faster.

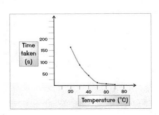
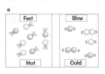
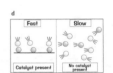
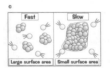
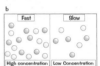

Q 3 Reacting particles must collide with enough energy in order to react. (There is an activation energy barrier.)

Page 37 — Experiments on Rates of Reaction

Q 1 a)

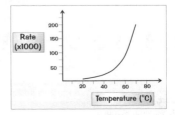

b) The higher the temperature, the less time is taken.
c)

Temperature (°C)	20	30	40	50	60	70
Time taken (s)	163	87	43	23	11	5
Rate (1/t)	0.0061	0.0115	0.0233	0.0435	0.0909	0.2000

d) The higher the temperature, the faster the rate of reaction.
e) Higher temperatures give particles more energy, which makes them move faster. Therefore there are more collisions, and as they have more energy, more of these collisions are successful. Both mean a faster reaction rate.

Q 2

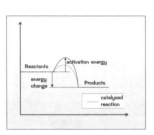

Q 3 a)

Volume of sodium thiosulphate (cm³)	50	40	30	20	10
Volume of water (cm³)	0	10	20	30	40
Time taken (s)	80	101	137	162	191
Rate (1/t)	0.0125	0.0099	0.0073	0.0062	0.0052

b)

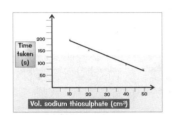

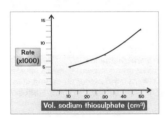

c) The greater the concentration the faster the reaction.
d) Higher concentration means there are more particles available for a collision and so available to react.

Page 38 — Catalysts and Enzymes

Q 1 a) Food spoilage is caused by reactions of bacteria and fungi.
b) The temperature in the fridge is about 5 °C and this slows the bacteria's reactions.
c) Freezing reduces the temperature further and effectively stops the spoilage reactions. Microbes cannot grow when the available water in the food is frozen.

Q 2 i) Biological detergents may contain protein-digesting and fat-digesting enzymes.
ii) To make yoghurt, the lactose in milk is converted to lactic acid by enzymes produced by bacteria (such as Lactobacillus). In cheese making, a variety of bacterial enzymes produce different textures and tastes.
iii) Amylase is used to break down starch into glucose and maltose, the sugars which most sweets are made from.

Q 3 a) i) Tubes 2 & 3 — Trypsin does not work on the protein on film B - enzymes are substrate specific.
ii) Tubes 2 & 4 - boiling stops the enzyme working.
iii) Tubes 2 & 5 - some substances can block or inhibit the action of enzymes.
b) Tube 1 is included as a control to show that film does not disintegrate of its own accord.

Q 4 a) About pH 8.
b) The shape of the active site changes — the enzyme is denatured. At pH1 and pH14 nearly all of the enzymes will be denatured and will not be able to catalyse the reaction.

Answers — Modules CD1 and CD2

Q5 Fish are cold-blooded — if their catalase enzyme needed 37°C to work, they wouldn't get rid of much hydrogen peroxide.

Page 39 — Enzymes

Q1 a) glucose → ethanol + carbon dioxide + energy
b) $C_6H_{12}O_6 \rightarrow 2\ C_2H_5OH + 2CO_2 + energy$
c)

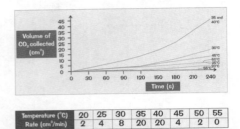

Temperature (°C)	20	25	30	35	40	45	50	55
Rate (cm³/min)	2	4	8	20	20	4	2	0

d) Optimum temperature is between 35 and 40 °C.
e) Above the optimum temperature the enzyme is denatured.
f) Fermentation products - beer, wine, bread.
g) Ethanoic acid (vinegar).

Q2 a) Pasteurised milk is used to make yoghurt and cheese.
b) Fresh milk contains other bacteria, which may spoil the foodstuff.
c) Cheese — lactic acid producing bacteria make the milk go acidic then further bacteria activity gives a sour (mature) taste and texture. Yoghurt — enzymes produced by bacteria make lactic acid (giving a sour taste). Lactic acid is produced in these fermentation processes rather than alcohol.

Module CD2 — Energy in Chemistry

Page 40 — The Atmosphere

Q1 No. Little oxygen and too many toxic gases like sulphur dioxide, ammonia and methane.

Q2 solidified, volcanoes, water vapour, ammonia, degassing, oceans, carbon dioxide, evolved, oxygen, photosynthesis

Q3 (i) Oxygen: 21%
(ii) Nitrogen: 78%
(iii) Carbon dioxide: 0.035%

Q4 a) Carbon dioxide.
b) Carbon dioxide + water → glucose + oxygen
c) $6CO_2 + 6H_2O \rightarrow C_6H_{12}O_6 + 6O_2$
d) Endothermic

Q5 The green plants, which undergo photosynthesis.

Page 41 — The Atmosphere

Q1 glucose + oxygen → carbon dioxide + water

Q2 Oxygen produced by early plants removed ammonia from the atmosphere producing nitrogen gas, which explains the increase in the amount of nitrogen in the air. Methane reacted with oxygen to form carbon dioxide, thus eliminating it from the air.

Q3 fossil fuel + oxygen → carbon dioxide + water

Q4 a)

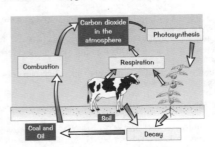

b) Processes such as respiration and combustion which remove oxygen from and release carbon dioxide into the atmosphere are counteracted by processes such as photosynthesis which remove CO_2 and release O_2.

Q5 CO_2 levels will increase and this could add to the Greenhouse Effect and cause global warming.

Q6 Trees in the forests photosynthesise, removing carbon dioxide from the atmosphere. If they are cut down, carbon dioxide levels will rise.

Page 42 — Crude Oil

Q1 a) A combination of different substances which have been mixed up without any chemical reaction taking place and so are not chemically bonded to each other.
b) Different sized hydrocarbon molecules.
c) A compound formed from carbon atoms and hydrogen atoms covalently bonded together. Hydrocarbons are fuels.
d) Methane, butane, propane, ethane, ethene, etc.
e) Because it is a mixture of lots of different substances, which all behave differently and have different properties.
f) We cannot make more oil to replace the oil that we use. Eventually oil supplies will run out.
g) **Advantages** - 1 Produces lots of energy for the cost. 2 Available in liquid form, which is light, and therefore easy to transport. 3 The main products (CO_2, H_2O) are non toxic. **Disadvantages** - 1 Produces CO_2, which contributes to the Greenhouse Effect. 2 They are non-renewable. 3 Minor products are toxic or highly damaging to the environment (CO, SO_2, Pb products from leaded petrol).

Q2 a) Energy.
b) Move around more quickly.
c) When the temperature is high enough the molecules have enough energy to overcome the intermolecular forces and escape from the liquid.

Q3 a) There is a limited amount, ie. oil will eventually run out.
b) Try not to waste it and cut down on its use; use renewable energy resources instead.
c) Try to prevent oil spillages; promote public transport (more efficient use of petrol); invest in renewable energy resources eg. solar power, wind power; more legislation and education.

Page 43 — Fractional Distillation

Q1 A mixture of different hydrocarbons.

Q2 A fuel formed from the fossilised remains of plants and/or animals.

Q3 Missing labels: A = petrol; B = naphtha; C = kerosene; D = diesel; E = engine oil/lubricating oil.

Q4 a) Vaporises easily.
b) Sets on fire easily.
c) Purifying.
d) Turns from a liquid to a gas.
e) Different components of a mixture, which have been separated from the mixture by distillation.
f) A process of separation, involving heating a mixture of liquids until one component vaporises, then cooling it to condense the vapour and collecting the resultant liquid.
g) Thick liquid.
h) Gases such as butane or propane which can be used as bottled gas.
i) A series of covalently bonded carbon atoms as found in molecules such as hydrocarbons.

Q5 a) Boiling point increases as length increases. The intermolecular forces between longer hydrocarbon molecules are larger and need more energy to break.
b) fractional distillation, hydrogen/ carbon, carbon/hydrogen, stronger, intermolecular.
c) Because once crude oil has been separated into its different fractions, each of these fractions has a very important use, e.g. refinery gases, petrol, jet fuel, diesel.

The Answers

Answers — Module CD2

d) As the length increases, flammability decreases.
e) As length increases, volatility decreases.
f) Short.

Page 44 — Hydrocarbons

Q1 a)

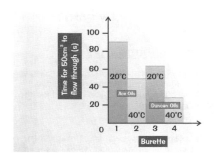

b) Ace oil.
c) Ace oil.
d) The viscosity will fall.
e) Do the experiment at the average temperature of a car engine.
f) Long chain, but not too long.
g) It might solidify or become too viscous.

Q2 i) methane + oxygen → carbon dioxide + water
$CH_4 + 2O_2 \rightarrow CO_2 + 2H_2O$
ii) ethane + oxygen → carbon dioxide + water
$2C_2H_6 + 7O_2 \rightarrow 4CO_2 + 6H_2O$
iii) propane + oxygen → carbon dioxide + water
$C_3H_8 + 5O_2 \rightarrow 3CO_2 + 4H_2O$
Oxidation (combustion),

Q3 a) The products of incomplete combustion include carbon monoxide (CO) which is a poisonous, odourless, colourless gas.
b) Complete combustion produces more heat and less soot.

Page 45 — Alkanes

Q1

Name	Formula	Melting Point(°C)	Boiling Point(°C)	Structural Formula
Methane	CH_4	-182	-164	H H-C-H H
Ethane	C_2H_6	-183	-89	H H H-C-C-H H H
Propane	C_3H_8	-190	-42	H H H H-C-C-C-H H H H
Butane	C_4H_{10}	-138	0	H H H H H-C-C-C-C-H H H H H
Pentane	C_5H_{12}	-130	36	H H H H H H-C-C-C-C-C-H H H H H H
Hexane	C_6H_{14}	-95	69	H H H H H H H-C-C-C-C-C-C-H H H H H H H

Q2 a) i) None listed.
ii) Pentane, hexane.
iii) Butane, propane, ethane, methane.
b) carbon: 5, hydrogen: 12
c) The more carbon atoms the alkane has, the higher its boiling point.
d) Because, if the chains are heavier and longer, they have stronger intermolecular forces and need more heat (energy) to break free from each other.

Q3 a) & b)

H H H
| | |
H—C—C≡C—H   O=C=O
| | |
H H H
O=O   H—O—H

c) $C_3H_8 + 5O_2 \rightarrow 3CO_2 + 4H_2O$

Page 46 — Energy Transfer in Reactions

Q1 a) Energy (heat), exothermic, energy (heat), endothermic.
b) exothermic, given out, endothermic, taken in,
c) ΔH, endothermic, negative.
d) energy, exothermic, endothermic, energy, break, energy, made.

Q2 a) Breaking bonds C-H x 5 = 413 x 5 = 2065;
C-O x 1 = 360; O-H x 1 = 463; C-C x 1=346;
Total =3234 kJ/mol
O=O x 3 = 497 x 3 = 1491
Total = 3234 + 1491 = 4725 kJ/mol.
b) Released on making:
4 x C=O = 740 x 4 = 2960;
6 x O-H = 6 x 463 = 2778;
Total energy released = 5738kJ/mol.
c) Overall energy change:
Energy in − Energy out = 4725 − 5738 = −1013 kJ/mol
d) A negative value means exothermic reaction.

Q3 a) 4 x C-H (413) = 1652 kJ/mol
2 x 0=0 (497) = 994 kJ/mol   Total =2646 kJ/mol
b) 2 x C=0 (740) = 1480 kJ/mol
4 x O-H (463) = 1852 kJ/mol   Total =3332 kJ/mol
c) Overall energy change
= energy in − energy out
= 2646 - 3332
= -686 kJ/mol (exothermic)
d) exothermic.
e) $4CH_4 + 6O_2 \rightarrow CO_2 + 8H_2O + 2CO + C$

Page 47 — Energy Transfer in Reactions

Q1 a&b)

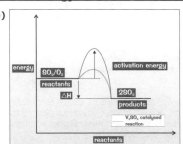

c) Exothermic.

Q2 a) Breaking one N≡N bond needs 945 kJ/mol.
b) Breaking the H-H bond needs 435 kJ/mol.
c) Making the N-H bond releases 389 kJ/mol.
d)

$$N≡N + 3\times(H–H) \rightleftharpoons 2\times \left(\begin{array}{c} H \\ | \\ N \\ / \ \backslash \\ H \quad H \end{array} \right)$$

e) Breaking reactant bonds needs
N ≡ N + (3 x H-H) = 945 + (3 x 435) = 2250 kJ/mol
f) Making product releases
6 x N-H = 6x389 = 2334 kJ/mol
g) Overall energy change is 2250 - 2334 = -84 kJ/mol
More energy is released. It is exothermic, overall energy change is -84 kJ/mol.

Q3 a) Copper is a good conductor of heat — this means that most of the heat will be transferred efficiently to the water.
b) Energy supplied = mass × SHC × temperature change
Mass = 200g, SHC of water = 4.18 J/°C/g, temperature change = 25.7°C
200 × 4.18 × 25.7 = 21485.2 J
Energy supplied per gram = Energy supplied/fuel mass
21485.2 ÷1.6 = 13428.25 J/g
Answer: 13.43 kJ/g.
c) A lot of the heat from the fuel is lost to the surroundings, and in heating the calorimeter.
d) Any two from: availability, storage, cost, toxicity, pollution, ease of use.

Answers — Module CD3

Module CD3 — Rocks and Metals

Page 48 — Plate Tectonics

Q 1 a) A: crust, B: mantle, C: inner core, D: outer core
b) Iron and nickel.
c) Mantle and outer core.
d) By studying the seismic waves from earthquakes — can tell changes in density from bending of waves. (Accept any sensible answer along those lines)
e) Inner and outer core (because they're made up of iron and nickel).
f) Lithosphere.

Q 2 The mantle is a layer of rock between the **core** and the **crust**. It has a **different** density and a different composition from the rock in the **crust**.

Q 3 The rock nearer the crust is relatively cold and rigid. The rock nearer the core is hot and non-rigid so it can flow at greater depths.

Q 4 The inner parts of the Earth must be denser than the rocks that make up the crust.

Q 5 C: 2 cm every year.

Q 6 Mountain ranges are gradually **worn down** by weathering and **erosion** but the movement of the Earth's crust over a very long time forms new **mountains**.

Page 49 — Plate Tectonics

Q 1 Mountains are eroded and particles wash into the sea. They settle and form sediment, which gets compressed over long periods of time to form sedimentary rocks.

Q 2 a) Fault caused one side to sink and/or one side to rise then pressure caused one side to tilt.
b) Ripple effect caused by movements of sea.
c) Folding, caused by pressure from both sides.

Q 3 Mountain belts were formed by movements of the Earth's **crust**. This process created **metamorphic** rocks — which are evidence of the high **temperatures** and pressures involved with the movements.

Q 4 Igneous.

Page 50 — Plate Boundaries

Q 1 a) Push towards each other, push away from each other.
b) Plates don't slide smoothly past each other — huge forces build up as they try to move, then when they do move, it's very sudden and very powerful.
c) Build earthquake-proof buildings, try to predict when they are going to happen, etc. (Accept any sensible answer.)

Q 2 Gujarat has more temporary housing and shanty towns, San Francisco has built many earthquake-proof buildings, Gujarat has a much higher population density, etc. (Accept any sensible answers.)

Q 3

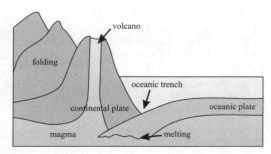

a) The oceanic plate starts to melt into the magma.
b) A subduction zone is where the oceanic plate is pushed under the continental plate.
c) Continental plate gets squashed and folded — forming mountains.
d) Earthquakes: plates moving against each other. Volcanoes: increased pressure from rocks melting so magma is forced to the surface.
e) (drawing of lava and ash coming out of volcano)
f) One example is the west coast of South America — the Andes were formed this way. (Accept any other correct examples.)

Page 51 — Plate Boundaries

Q 1 a) Magma rises to the surface and cools, forming solid rock.
b) Basalt — formed when magma cools quickly.
c) Mid-Atlantic Ridge (down... you guessed it... the middle of the Atlantic Ocean).
d) Tidal waves/tsunami.

Q 2 As the **plates** move apart, liquid **magma (or rock)** is pushed up to fill the gap. As it solidifies, the **iron** particles contained in it align themselves with the Earth's **magnetic** field, and set in position. This provides a record of the Earth's magnetic field at the time when the **magma (or rock)** cooled.
Scientists know that the Earth's magnetic field changes **direction** about every 500 000 years. This means that on either side of the ridge there are bands of alternate **magnetic** polarity. These bands were discovered about 40 years ago, and provided strong **evidence** for continental drift.

Page 52 — The Reactivity Series of Metals

Q 1 a) Metals put in order of reactivity (beginning with the most reactive).
b) Most violent reaction or fastest reaction.
c) Potassium, Sodium, Aluminium, Zinc, Iron, Copper, Gold.
d) $1 \rightarrow C$, $2 \rightarrow A$, $3 \rightarrow D$, $4 \rightarrow B$.

Q 2 Carbon is between Al and Zn.

Q 3 a) Above it.
b) Carbon is above iron in the reactivity series — the carbon in CO removes the oxygen from the iron.
c) Iron oxide + Carbon monoxide → Iron + Carbon dioxide.

Q 4 They are very unreactive, so do not combine with other elements easily.

Q 5 Its extraction is expensive as lots of electricity is needed for electrolysis of the ore. It can't be extracted in any other way because it's too reactive.

Q 6 Because gold and silver are unreactive, whereas sodium is very reactive, and would react violently with any water which it came into contact with (even the moisture on your hand — eeek!).

Q 7 a) Very high.
b) Rubidium, Caesium, or Francium.
c) X between Potassium and Magnesium.

Page 53 — Metal Ores

Q 1 a) mineral containing enough metal to make it worth extracting from the ground.
b) Haematite (iron ore); Bauxite (aluminium ore); Malachite (copper ore).
c) As pure metal.
d) Gold, platinum, silver.
e) As compounds (metal ores).

Q 2 a) Metal ore detected in ground.
b) Earth containing ore dug from ground.
c) Waste earth removed to concentrate ore.
d) Carbon reduction.
e) Electrolysis.
f) Pure metal.

Q 3 Electrolysis of Molten Ore: potassium, aluminium, calcium, magnesium.
Reduction of Metal Ore With Carbon: zinc, iron.

Answers — Module CD3

Occurs Naturally: gold, (iron — v.rare).

Q4 a) Zinc or Copper.
b) Because magnesium is higher in the reactivity series than carbon, so cannot be reduced by it.

Page 54 — Metal Ores

Q1 **a)** A **b)** B, D or F **c)** C **d)** E **e)** B or D **f)** F

Q2 a) It fixes bricks together.
b) A combination of different substances which have been mixed up without any chemical reaction taking place and so are not chemically bonded to each other.

Q3 **a)** Calcium carbonate. **b)** Sedimentary. **c)** Strong in compression, easy to cut. **d)** Cement. **e)** Concrete. (There are loads of uses – building roads, making building blocks, stepping in and leaving your footprints to set, etc)

Q4 a) pottery **b)** glass **c)** aluminium **d)** chlorine **e)** iron

Q5 The limestone removes sand (silicon dioxide) which is the main impurity in the iron ore.

Page 55 — Extracting Iron — The Blast Furnace

Q1 a) Because iron is lower in the Reactivity Series than carbon, so can be reduced by it. Sodium and aluminium are above carbon in the Reactivity Series.
b) Haematite.
c) Oxygen.
d) Fe_2O_3

Q2 a) Iron ore, coke, limestone.
b) To make the coke burn faster than usual (and increase temperature).
c) So that the pure iron is molten and can be tapped off.
d) A = (molten) iron; B = (molten) slag.

Q3 a) By the combustion of coke (carbon).
b) $C + O_2 \rightarrow CO_2$

Q4 Reacts with unburnt coke to form carbon monoxide.

Q5 a) $3CO + Fe_2O_3 \rightarrow 3CO_2 + 2Fe$
b) It has been reduced.
c) Liquid.
d) It runs to the bottom of the furnace where it is tapped off.

Q6 a) Sand (silicon dioxide).
b) $CaCO_3 \rightarrow CaO + CO_2$
c) $CaO + SiO_2 \rightarrow CaSiO_3$
d) Road building and fertilisers.

Page 56 — Extracting Aluminium

Q1

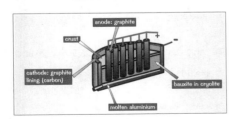

Q2 Aluminium is much more **reactive** than carbon so is extracted from its **ore** using electrolysis. Aluminium is the most abundant metal in the Earth's crust, and is joined up with other elements, rock and clays, which make it **difficult** to extract. The main ore of aluminium is called **bauxite**, which is impure aluminium oxide. It is purified, then dissolved in molten **cryolite** (another ore of aluminium) which lowers the melting point from over 2000°C to about **900** °C. Electricity passes through the melted ore separating the **aluminium** from the oxygen. The overall equation is:
Aluminium oxide → **aluminium + oxygen**.

Q3 a) Because the impurities might be electrolysed instead of the aluminium.

b) To reduce the temperature needed.
c) Lowering the temperature required down to about 900 °C, which is cheaper and safer.
d) At the cathode: $Al^{3+} + 3e^- \rightarrow$ **Al**
At the anode: $2O^{2-} \rightarrow$ **O_2** $+ 4e^-$
e) i) Cathode.
ii) Anode.
f) At the anode the oxygen being released reacts with the graphite to form CO_2. This wears away the anode.

Page 57 — Extracting Aluminium

Q1 a) (Clockwise from top): stepladders, compact discs, window frames, cans, aeroplanes, foil, saucepans, bottle tops.
b) Light, corrosion-resistant, easily alloyed, high thermal conductivity, shiny/reflective, malleable.

Q2 **Crossword answers:**
Across: 3. purified 4. cathode 5. bauxite
Down: 1. cryolite 2. melting

Page 58 — Purifying Copper by Electrolysis

Q1 a) Electrolysis.
b) It is cheaper. You don't have to dig up the ore, purify it and use electrolysis to extract the copper.
It conserves resources. Copper is a finite resource. Recycling helps preserve supplies.

Q2 a) TRUE
b) FALSE - it's less reactive
c) FALSE - it's easy
d) TRUE
e) TRUE
f) FALSE - it's pure copper

Q3 a) –ve cathode; +ve anode.
b) They are positively charged and so are attracted by the negatively charged cathode.
c) Electrons.
d) $Cu^{2+} + 2e^- \rightarrow Cu$
e) $Cu \rightarrow Cu^{2+} + 2e^-$

Q4 **Electrolysis** is the **splitting** of a compound by passing **electricity** through it. It is used to **purify** metals. **Copper** can be purified in this way. Copper sulphate solution is the **electrolyte**, which produces **copper** ions and sulphate ions. The impure copper is attached to the **positive** electrode, the **anode**. This produces **copper (or positive)** ions which are attracted to the negative cathode. Here they gain two **electrons** to become **copper** metal. A **sludge** from the impure **copper / anode** forms underneath the **anode**.

Page 59 — Ions

Q1 a) An atom or molecule that is charged because it has gained or lost electrons.
b) Na^+, O^{2-} or any other sensible example.
c) Atoms are electrically **neutral** because they have equal numbers of **protons** and electrons (**–ve**). If electrons are taken away from an atom, then it becomes **positively charged** because it has less electrons than protons. If electrons are added to an atom, it becomes **negatively charged** because it then has more electrons than protons.

Q2 **a)** Kr **b)** Cl^- **c)** CO_2 **d)** MgO or CO_2
e) SO_4^{2-}, Cl^- or Mg^{2+} **f)** SO_4^{2-}

Q3 Decomposition of a salt using electricity.

Q4 $2Cl^- \rightarrow Cl_2 + 2e^-$

Q5 a) The electrostatic attraction between oppositely charged ions formed by losing or gaining electrons.
b) 1–
c) 1+
d) A cation is a positively charged ion and an anion is a negatively charged ion.

Answers — Module PD1

Module PD1 — Waves

Page 60 — Waves

Q 1 a) Longitudinal, transverse.
   b) Frequency, hertz (Hz).
   c) Period, seconds (s).
   d) Amplitude.
   e) Crest or peak.
   f) Trough.
   g) Speed, metres per second (m/s).
   h) Refraction.
   i) Diffraction.

Q 2 The particles in an ocean wave move up and down.

Q 3 The distance of a full wave cycle eg. from crest to crest, trough to trough, or between any two identical points. Metres (usually).

Q 4 a) Oscillation.
   b) Shake hand faster.
   c) Increase distance of hand movement.
   d) Insufficient tension in the string means that a wave will not be transmitted effectively.

Q 5 Energy.

Q6 a) 5 s   **b)** 0.2 Hz
   c) 3 m   **d)** 3 m
   e) 5 s   **f)** 0.6 m
   g) 0.6 m/s   **h)** Up and down.

Page 61 — Waves

Q 7 Correct equations are:
Speed = frequency × wavelength.
$v = f\lambda$
Wavelength = speed / frequency.
$\lambda = v/f$
Frequency = speed / wavelength.
$f = v/\lambda$

Q8 **a)** decreases.
   b) increases.
   c) decreases.
   d) increases.

Q9 **a)** Straight line at zero metres.
   b) **i)** A, G
      ii) D, I
      iii) B, C, H
      iv) F, E
      v) A, G, D, I
      vi) A, G, D, I
      vii) C, F, H
      viii) A, G, D, I
   c) 1 m, 10 m, 1 Hz

Q 10 $f = v/\lambda = 1.33 \times 10^5$ Hz

Q11 **a)** The ruler is at the same point each time the light flashes.
   b) 0.02 s (approx.)
   c) 24 flashes per sec. Now the flashes catch the ruler in the same position every two cycles.

Page 62 — Sound Waves

Q 1 A vibration.

Q 2 Drum-skin, violin-string, loudspeaker-cone, voice-vocal cords.

Q 3 As a longitudinal wave through the air.

Q 4

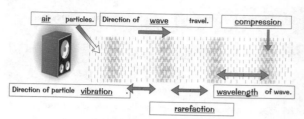

Q 5 a) 333 m/s
   b) 1.67 m
   c) Frequency is 10 times greater.
    The ratio of the wavelengths is 1:10.

Page 63 — Light Waves

Q 1 a) Reflect.
   b) Clear, shiny.
   c) Diffuse, dull.
   d) Reflection, equal, incidence.

Q 2 A ray.

Q 3 The normal.

Q 4

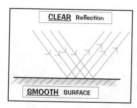

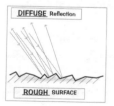

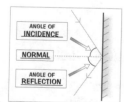

Q 5 Person 1 can see statue C and D. Person 2 can see A and D.

Q 6 a) Diagram 1: X.
   b) Diagram 2: B.

Q 7 Towards, away from.

Page 64 — Diffraction

Q 1 a) Spread out, gap, obstacle.
   b) Diffraction.
   c) Smaller.
   d) Bigger.

Q 2 Because sound has much larger wavelengths than light, it will diffract around objects that appear to be 'ordinary sized' (i.e. doors, tables etc.). Light, with its much smaller wavelength, will diffract significantly only around much smaller objects.

Answers — Module PD1

Q 3

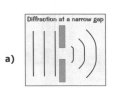

a)

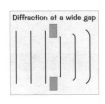

b)

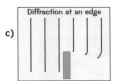

c)

d)

Page 65 — Total Internal Reflection

Q1 a)

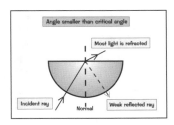

b)

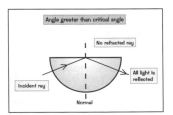

Q 2 a) The ray is parallel to the normal of the outer surface of the prism.
b)

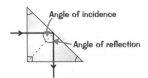

c) 45° to the inner surface
d) They must be the same.

Q3 a)

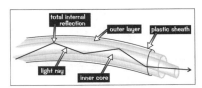

b) •signal doesn't need boosting so often,
•cable of the same diameter can carry *much* more information,
•signals are relatively secure,
•signals safe from electrical interference,
•fibres made from glass — cheaper, more plentiful than copper.

Q 4 An endoscope uses two bundles of optical fibres to send light into and get images out of inside the body. They can be used for "keyhole surgery", where only a very small incision is made into the body.

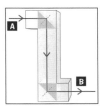

b) Light always hits the prism along the normal, so there is no dispersion.
c) At B.
d) You will be able to see around higher obstructions.

Q 2 In a submarine (especially for viewing the sea surface whilst submerged).
Viewing over a crowd. You can see lots of people using them at golf tournaments.

Q3 a) To make them short enough to be held and used easily.
b)

c) The mirrors won't absorb as much light as prisms.

d) Light incident on the prism within a certain angle will be totally internally reflected.

Q 4 a) Provided incident ray reflects off two surfaces, the reflected ray will be displaced from, but parallel to, the incident ray.
b) Incident ray from E meets the surface at an angle below the critical angle and so it will not reflect back towards same direction from which it came.
c) It will not be reflected and will pass through the reflector.

Page 67 — Ultrasound

Q 1 Frequency, ultrasound.

Q 2 a) 0.0132m = 1.32cm.
b) 0.011m = 1.1cm.
c) 0.0066m = 0.66cm.
d) 0.0033m = 0.33cm.

Q 3

Application	Category of use	Ultrasound used to	Basic principles
Removal of kidney stones	Medical	Shatter stones allowing them to be passed out in urine	Use of energy in ultrasound to physically alter material
Quality control	Industrial	Check for cracks in metal castings	Detection of reflected ultrasound to build image
Removal of tartar	Medical	Break up tartar deposits on teeth	Use of energy in ultrasound to physically alter material
Sonar	Military / Scientific	Measure distances to objects or map the sea bed	Detection of reflected ultrasound to build image
Pre-natal screening	Medical	Image the foetus	Detection of reflected ultrasound to build image
Cleaning	Industrial	Cleaning delicate mechanisms without dismantling them	Use of energy in ultrasound to physically alter material

Answers — Modules PD1 and PD2

Q4 a) Ultrasound is unlikely to cause any damage to tissues.
b) Ultrasound avoids having to dismantle them and reduces the risk of damage.
c) Surgery is more likely to damage the kidney permanently, and ultrasound will not risk damaging other body parts either.
d) Flaws could cause the material to break. Ultrasound detects tiny cracks, without damage.
e) Tartar encourages the build-up of bacteria, increasing the risk of gum disease. Ultrasound can be used to loosen tartar in difficult-to-reach places.

Page 68 — Seismic Waves

Q1 a)

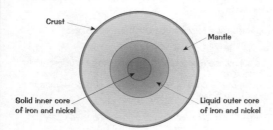

Crust
Mantle
Solid inner core of iron and nickel
Liquid outer core of iron and nickel

b) Because we can only drill about 10km or so into the crust of the Earth, which is not very far, so seismic waves are really the only way of investigating the inner structure.

Q2 a) A transverse wave that will only travel through solids.
b) Shadow zone.
c) These waves can't travel through the liquid outer core.
d) Solid.

Q3 a) Density.
b) The density is continually changing, causing the wave to bend as it slows down or speeds up.

Q4 They are longitudinal, faster than S-waves, and travel through both solids and liquids.

Q5 a) Mantle and the outer core.
b) There is a sudden change of density there.
c) Between points R and S and between points P and Q.
d) They travel through both solids and liquids.

Q6 P-wave; travels faster.

Page 69 — The EM Spectrum

Q1 a) Spectrum, speed, vacuum, seven, radio waves, microwaves, infra-red, visible light, ultra violet, x-rays, gamma rays.
b) Radio, longest, gamma rays, shortest, visible light.

Q2 Correct: **a, c, e, h, i, j.**
f is debatable as X-rays are *relatively* safe compared with the high risks of investigative surgery including death under anaesthetic, post-operative shock and infection, but are still highly hazardous.
b) Replace microwaves with infra red.
d) Replace only visible light with all EM waves.
g) Replace infra red with ultraviolet.
f) Ultrasound might be suggested as an alternative to X-rays for medical imaging but the two techniques give very different results which is why X-rays are still widely used.

Q3 a) Order in the diagram should read:
Gamma rays:	10^{-12} m	3×10^{20} Hz
X-rays:	10^{-10} m	3×10^{18} Hz
Ultra Violet:	10^{-8} m	3×10^{16} Hz
Visible Light:	10^{-7} m	3×10^{15} Hz
Infrared:	10^{-5} m	3×10^{13} Hz
Microwaves:	10^{-2} m	3×10^{10} Hz
Radio waves:	10^{0} m	3×10^{8} Hz

b) 300,000,000 m/s.
c) See table above.
d) 1000.
e) 100,000.

Page 70 — The EM Spectrum

Q1

Type of Radiation	Effects on Living Tissue	Uses
Gamma	• kills living cells in high doses • lower doses can cause cells to become cancerous • kills cancerous cells	• kill bacteria in food • sterilise medical equipment • treat tumours
X-Ray	• kills living cells in high doses • lower doses can cause cells to become cancerous	• imaging internal structures in the body • studying the atomic structure of materials
UV	• kills living cells in high doses • lower doses can cause cells to become cancerous • causes tanning	• fluorescent tubes • tanning • security marking
Visible	• activates sensitive cells in the retina	• seeing • optical fibre
IR	• causes burning of tissues	• radiant heaters • grills • remote controls • thermal imaging
Microwave	• heating of water in tissues can cause "burning"	• satellite communication • cooking
Radio	• probably none	• communication • broadcasting • radar

Q2 a) Heat; electricity (alternating current with the same frequency as the radiation itself).
b) More.
c) By covering her skin with a barrier, e.g. clothes, sun lotion, or by reducing the amount of time she spends in the sun. Infrared radiation can damage cells, Ultra-violet radiation can cause cancer.
d) By using lead screens, and limiting himself to short doses.

Page 71 — Radioactive Substances

Q1 a) Hand stops alpha, thin aluminium stops beta. Thick lead stops gamma.
b) Alpha particles are relatively slow moving and are charged. They also lose energy quickly in collisions (while ionising the atoms of the material).

Q2 a) A tracer is a substance used to follow the movements of a particular chemical. (The tracer should flow in the same way as the chemical of interest and be easily detectable).
b) The thyroid gland. This is where iodine is absorbed in the body.
c) Gamma radiation.
d) **1.** Alpha particles would be absorbed in the neck preventing detection.
2. The radiation would be more harmful.

Q3 a) Gamma.
b) Kills cells.
c) To prevent killing healthy cells.
d) Not all the cancerous cells are killed.
e) Too many healthy cells may be killed.

Q4 a) Gamma rays kill them.
b) The doses of gamma rays kill healthy cells too — destroying a large number of cells can disrupt life processes, like fighting infection, and the patient can become ill.
c) The location(s) of the tumour(s) need to be identified accurately. The minimum dose needed to just kill the tumour(s) and the course of treatment also need to be worked out.

Module PD2 — Energy in the Home

Page 72 — Heat Transfer

Q1 a) All three.
b) Conduction.
c) Convection.
d) Radiation.
e) Radiation.
f) Convection.

Answers — Module PD2

Q 2 a)

b) Heat energy moves along the bar by conduction, so all readings are higher than they were initially. It is also radiated away from the conductor, so the temperature will be nearer the background temperature the further you are from the burner.

c)

Q 3 solids, close, vibrate, neighbouring, good, electrons, carry, collide.

Q 4 expands, decreases, rises, decreases, contracting, higher, falls.

Page 73 — Heat Transfer

Q 1 a) The dull, black surface is a better absorber than the shiny, silver surface — so the dull, black beaker absorbs more heat and the temperature rises faster.

b) The dull, black surface cools faster because it radiates away heat at a faster rate — ie. it is a better emitter of heat radiation.

Q 2 a) More heat is lost by radiation on a clear night, so frosts are more likely (clouds would reflect a lot of this heat back).

b) Convection will ensure that the heated water will rise to the outflow at the top, while the cooler water will sink to the bottom, where it can be heated, and so the heat is evenly distributed.

c) Snow is an insulator (it traps air and also reflects radiation back), so heat is trapped.

d) Shiny colours are poor radiators, and so keep the tea hot longer.

e) Air is trapped in the feathers, giving an insulating layer.

f) Heat energy is conducted into the pliers, stopping the circuit board getting too hot.

Q 3 a)–d) These all rely on trapped air. The trapped air can no circulate and so convection is reduced. Air is also a good insulator and so reduces conduction. The solid material will also act as a barrier against radiation and is an insulator but these tend to be secondary effects.

e) Double glazing — the air gap will reduce conduction.

f) Draught-proofing — strips of foam and plastic around doors prevent warm air escaping and cold air entering the house.

g) Thermostats — by preventing the house from being over-warmed they reduce all three types of heat loss.

Q 4 Many possibilities including:

Name of substance	Conductor/ Insulator	Used for
copper	conductor	saucepan bodies
aluminium	conductor	kettles
iron	conductor	cooling fins
foam	insulator	flasks
porcelain	insulator	crockery
cork	insulator	table mats

Page 74 — Heat Transfer

Q 1 a) Plastic is a poor conductor. The lid prevents loss of heat by evaporation from the top.

b) Cork is a poor conductor; it also contains lots of air, which is also a poor conductor.

c) Glass is a poor conductor.

d) The vacuum will only allow heat transfer by radiation. No conduction or convection is possible.

e) The silver outer surface is a poor radiator of heat.

f) The silver surface is a poor absorber of heat radiation; it will reflect heat back in.

g) Air is a poor conductor.

h) The foam is a poor conductor of heat. It also prevents a lot of convection of the trapped air.

Q 2 a) Total units used per year: $365 \times 21.9 = 7993.5$ units
Total cost: $7993.5 \times 6p = £479.61$

b) To save money. For environmental considerations.

c) Loft insulation: $200 \div 50 = 4$ years
Double Glazing: $3000 \div 60 = 50$ years
Draft Proofing: $50 \div 50 = 1$ year
Cavity Wall Insulation: $600 \div 100 = 6$ years
Hot Water Tank Jacket: $10 \div 15 = {}^{2}/_{3}$ year = 8 months

d) **i)** They can afford every method except the double glazing.
ii) Total cost: £200+£50+£600+£10 = £860
iii) Total annual saving: £50+£50+£100+£15 = £215
iv) Payback time: $860 \div 215 = 4$ years

Page 75 — Domestic Electricity

Q 1 a) No. of units: 484, 666
Cost of electricity: £35.57, £48.95
Total bill: £45.06, £58.44
Vat @ 8%: £3.60, £4.68

b) Kilowatt hours (kWh).

c) 48000 (approximately), 28300 (approximately).

d) More electricity (units) used as it's colder/darker in winter.

Q 2 Electric cooker, kettle, electric heater, toaster. They all have heating elements.

Q 3 a) J, kJ, kWh, "Units".

b) W, kW.

c) 1/10

d) 1000

Q 4 1000 W, 3600 s, 1 kWh, 3600 000 J (=3.6 MJ)

Q 5 easy, appliances, toasters, pollution, storage, disadvantages, shock, power cut, cables, countryside.

Page 76 — Domestic Electricity

Q 1 take, previous, energy, voltage, energy, joules, twice.

Q 2 a) 1 kWh

b) 0.05 kWh

c) 0.25 kWh

d) 0.1 kWh

Q 3 a) 6 p

b) 0.1 p

c) £1.26

d) 67.5 p

e) £1.44

Q 4 a) Fire.

b) Vacuum cleaner.

c) Both the same.

d) Iron.

e) Immersion heater.

Q 5 a) CFL: £24, £34; Filament: £10, £126.

b) Cheaper, saves energy, saves oil/coal used to make electricity, fewer waste bulbs etc.

Answers — Modules PD2 and PD3

Page 77 — Domestic Electricity

Q1 a) night
b) storage heaters; day
c) dishwashers
d) cheaply
e) expensive
f) power stations

Q2 Total fixed charge cost: 90×14p=£12.60
Total cost of low-rate electricity: 350×3p=£10.50
Total cost of normal-rate electricity: 900×6p=£54.00

So total amount is: £12.60+£10.50+£54.00 = £77.10

Q3 a) Frayed wire, twisted flex, insulating tape is loose.
Rewire appliance.
b) Bare (live) terminal. Insert bulb (switch off first).
c) Overloaded with plugs due to a 3 way adaptor in another adaptor. Use a plug board or use other sockets.
d) Electrical appliance near water — would electrify the man in the bath. Don't use electrical appliances in the bathroom. Don't have plug sockets in the bathroom in the first place...

Q4 1. Trailing cable — can be dangerous near pets/children.
2. Cables near heat/water.
3. Water near sockets.
4. Poking things into sockets.
5. Damaged/wrongly wired plugs, appliances without covers.
6. Incorrect use of fuses.

Page 78 — Safety Features

Q1 A: neutral (blue), B: earth (green and yellow),
C: live (brown).

Q2 a) Pins/screws; robust and good conductors.
b) Case, cable grip; to insulate wires and cable.

Q3 1. Check wires are in the right places.
2. Check cable grip tight enough.
3. Check fuse in place.
4. Check bare wires aren't in contact with anything other than the screw and are not exposed.
5. Check screws are tight.

Q4 a) If a contact is made between live and the case, a high current will flow to earth blowing the fuse. If the earth connection is missing and the equipment is insulated from the ground the case will remain live until handled.
b) TVs have a plastic case which means that, even if a contact is made between the live wire and the case, there will be no current to earth through a person touching the TV.

Q5 Live — carries a high voltage.
Neutral — is always at 0 V. It is the wire which completes the circuit.

Q6 voltage, alternating, 230, live, neutral, earth, safety.

Q7 a) To protect the user and the appliance in the event of an abnormally high current eg. short circuit. The fuse will cut off the power supply.
b)

metal wire

c) Fuse wire melts and breaks (3 A wire is too thin to handle 6 A currents).
d) Would blow straight away.
e) The earth wire allows a large current to flow, and this blows the fuse, cutting off the supply of electricity.

Page 79 — Safety Features

Q1 5, 5, 13, 5, 13, 5 (all amps).

Q2 **1.** Should be 230 V AC not 220 V DC. **2.** Fuse should be on live. **3.** Switch should be on live. **4.** The earth symbol is upside down.

Q3 wired, fuse, earth, blown, expert (electrician), replace, cover.

Q4 a) Hairdryer stops working, lights in lounge, kitchen and dining room go out.
b) Lights work but hairdryer doesn't.
c) Hairdryer works but lights don't.

Module PD3 — Forces and Motion

Page 80 — Velocity and Acceleration

Q1 a) 10 m/s **b)** 20 m/s
c) 1.5 m/s **d)** 0.1 m/s

Q2 a) 17.14 m/s — he is probably right.
b) 10 s
c) 30 s

Q3 a) 2700 m **b)** 16250 m
c) 15000 m **d)** 17500 m

Q4 How, fast, direction, direction.

Q5 a) 20 m/s
b) The car will be speeding up and slowing down in traffic. It will take corners slowly, etc.
c) 30 km

Q6 a) 42 m/s **b)** 1.3 m/s

Q7 a) 36 km **b)** 125 km

Page 81 — Velocity and Acceleration

Q1 a) 8 hours. **b)** 8 minutes 20 seconds.

Q2 2 m/s East.

Q3 90 m/s South East.

Q4 a) 1.4 m/s North-East.
b) 1.7 m/s South-West.
c) 1.2 m/s including rest.
1.5 m/s excluding rest.

Q5 a) a is the acceleration, v is the final velocity, u is the initial velocity and t is the time taken.
b) m/s^2, m/s, m/s and s.
c) Acceleration is used to describe the **rate of change** in velocity. Its units are m/s^2. Velocity is used to describe the rate of change of position in m/s.

Q6 Acceleration, second, velocity, 3 m/s, acceleration, second, velocity, 4 m/s.

Q7 a) 54 km
b) 128 km/h, 35.6 m/s
c) 25 seconds
d) 7.2 km
e) 1.87 m/s^2

Page 82 — D-T and V-T Graphs

Q1 a) 225 metres.
b) The car continues to move at a steady velocity of 15 m/s.
c)

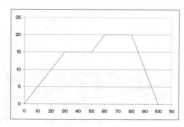

d) 0.5 m/s^2
e) 1 m/s^2
f) 600 m (Find the area under the graph for the last 40 seconds.)

Answers — Module PD3

Q2 a) 800 m
  b) 1.5 m/s²
  c) 500 m
  d) Riding at constant speed of 10 m/s.
  e) 1.5 km

Q3 a) Steady speed, then stationary, then steady speed in opposite direction.

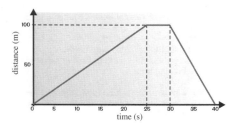

  b) 4 m/s
  c) 5 s
  d) 10 m/s

Page 83 — D-T and V-T Graphs

Q1 a), b)

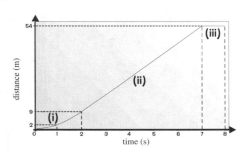

  c) 7.7 m/s
  d) 40.5 m
  e) 3.6 s

Q2

Feature on Graph	Distance/Time	Velocity/Time
Gradient equals	SPEED	ACCELERATION
Flat sections show	NOT MOVING	CONSTANT SPEED
Curves show	ACCELERATION	CHANGES IN ACCELERATION
Downhill section shows	MOVING BACKWARDS	DECELERATION
Area under the curve shows	NOT APPLICABLE	DISTANCE

Q3 a) 15 m/s
  b) 200 m
  c) 5 m/s
  d) Steady speed for first 20 s. Decelerates at 20 s, then continues at a lower steady speed until 40 s. Then steady speed in the opposite direction from 40 s to 60 s, coming back to where it started.

Q4

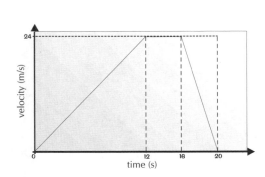

a) The car accelerates at a steady rate for 12 s, then travels steadily for 4 s before decelerating steadily to a halt in 4 s.
  b) 2 m/s²
  c) 2000 N
  d) 6 m/s²

Page 84 — Force Diagrams

Q1 a) Gravity or weight.
  b) Drag or air resistance or friction.
  c) Tension.
  d) Lift.
  e) Thrust or push or pull.
  f) Reaction force.

Q2 a) Weight (down) and reaction (up).
  b) The object is not accelerating.
  c) It would accelerate in the direction of that force.

Q3 a) Weight down, reaction up.
  b) Thrust forward, drag backwards (both equal).

Q4 Faster, unbalanced, greater, force, greater, smaller, thrust, drag, weight, reaction, downwards, drag, upwards.

Q5 a) It remains stationary.
  b) It slows down and eventually stops due to friction.
  c) It needs a thrust equal to the frictional forces exerted by the ground.

Page 85 — Force, Mass and Acceleration

Q1 a) 1.25 m/s²
  b) 4 m/s²
  c) 1.67 m/s²

Q2 a) Balanced forces — all forces cancel each other out. There is no resultant force.
      Velocity — speed in a particular direction.
  b)

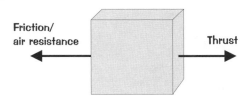

      The arrows should be the same length.
  c) Resultant force — combining all the separate forces gives the resultant force.
  d) Zero.

Q3 a) Newtons, kg, m/s²
  b) a=F/m
  c) m=F/a

Q4 a) 10 m/s²
  b) 20 m/s²
  c) 30 m/s²

Q5 a) (i) and (iii) **b)** (ii) **c)** (iv)

Q6 18 m/s

Q7 a) 450 N
  b) 450 N
  c) 1 m/s² in the opposite direction to Coco.

Page 86 — Force, Mass and Acceleration

Q1 a) 50 N right.
  b) 0.5 N up.
  c) 15 N up.

Answers — Module PD3

d) 0.05 N down.

Q 2 a) FALSE — if something moves with a steady speed, there must be no overall force on it.
b) TRUE.
c) TRUE.
d) FALSE — the bigger the force, the bigger the acceleration.
e) TRUE.
f) FALSE — to get a small mass to accelerate as much as a big mass, it needs a smaller force.

Q 3 a)

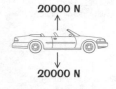

20000 N

20000 N

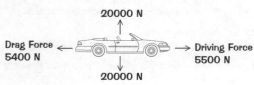

20000 N

Drag Force 5400 N — Driving Force 5500 N

20000 N

b) 2.75 m/s²
c) 0.05 m/s²

Q 4 Mass, acceleration, one newton, force, mass, double.

Q 5 a) 50 N
b) 125 N
c) 3200 N

Page 87 — Stopping Distances for Cars

Q 1 a) Thinking distance and braking distance.
b) Thinking distance — the distance the car travels between a hazard appearing and the driver applying the brakes.
Braking distance — the distance the car travels while the brakes are being applied.

Q 2 a) Greater.
b) Greater.

Q 3 22; 38; 17; 19; 55; 119

Q 4 a) Braking distance.
b) The curves given are only approximations. Accept if curve 1) is steeper than curve 2), either side of the original one.

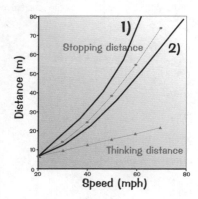

The thinking distance is the same in both cases.

Q 5 a) Any 4 of these 5:
Driver tiredness — when you are tired, you are less likely to notice things, and your reflexes are slowed.
Illness — as with tiredness.
Drugs/alcohol — as with tiredness.
Speed — thinking distance is all to do with the time it takes to react, so the faster you are going, the greater the thinking distance will be.
b) Speed — the faster you're going the further it takes to stop.
Mass — the more heavily loaded the car, the further it takes to stop.
Condition of tyre — tyres should have 1.6 mm of tread. Without this, the car skids very easily.
Condition of brakes — worn or faulty brakes will not provide as big a braking force.

Q 6 a) Friction with the road, which is what stops the car, is reduced in very wet or icy conditions. Other examples are leaves, mud, diesel spills, etc.
b) If the car is full of people and luggage, it will have more mass. This will increase the braking distance.
c) The faster you are going, the longer it takes to stop. You take longer to stop on a motorway than if you're driving at 30 mph in a city.
d) The braking force depends on the condition of the brakes in the car. If they are worn down, the force applied to stop the car will be less.

Page 88 — Moments

Q 1
a)   b)   c)

Q 2 a) Moment = Force × Perpendicular distance between the action of the force and the pivot.
b) Increase the force. Increase the perpendicular distance from the pivot.

Q 3 a) 0.75 Nm
b) 6 Nm
c) 24 Nm

Q 4 Equilibrium, equilibrium, clockwise, equals, anti-clockwise, 4, 60, 120, right.

Q 5 a) 50 cm
b) 1.8 N
c) 0.7 N
d) 60 cm

Q 6 a) The girder tips in the weasel's direction.
b) The system is in equilibrium.